Reality Bytes

Reality Bytes

A journey into the heart of youthwork
armed with only enthusiasm, hope
and a packet of chocolate biscuits

Nick Page

11 10 09 08 07 06 05   7 6 5 4 3 2 1

First published 2005 by Spring Harvest Publishing Division
and Authentic Media
9 Holdom Avenue, Bletchley, Milton Keynes, Bucks, MK1 1QR, UK
and 129 Mobilization Drive, Waynesboro, GA 30830-4575, USA
www.authenticmedia.co.uk

British Library Cataloguing in Publication Data
A catalogue record for this book is available from the British Library

ISBN 1-85078-618-6

The views expressed by the author do not necessarily represent the
views of the partner organisations.

Cover design by fourninezero design.
Typeset by Temple Design
Print Management by Adare Carwin
Printed and Bound by J. H. Haynes & Co. Ltd., Sparkford

Contents

From: Chris Francis@Tabernacle.ch.uk

To: Patricia Ryan, P.Ryan@bigplace.com

Subject: Hello!

Pat,

Well – here I am! The first full-time youthworker at this church. Having set my computer up, I can now get online again.

Life here has been manic since I arrived. My flat is great – on the ground floor, with plenty of room for the kids to meet.

Thanks for agreeing to be my 'mentor'. I can't tell you how much your advice and encouragement has supported me in the past. I know that there will be lots of people around here only too happy to give me the benefits of their advice and opinions, but to have someone objective, someone outside my work will be great. And the fact that we've known each other a long time means that you can say what you want to me – after all, you've never exactly held back before!

I think you're right about emails being the best way to keep in touch. It will give me a chance to reflect on things; I always find that putting my thoughts down on paper helps me get things in a clearer perspective. (Or putting them down on screen, to be more precise.)

Anyway, as I said, I'm settling in. This afternoon I'm going to go down to the church and have a proper look at the facilities. The letter from the church talked about a 'well-stocked youth resources' cupboard, so that seems a good place to start.

Cheers
Chris
Chris Francis – Youthworker
Briglimpton Tabernacle

From: Chris Francis@Tabernacle.ch.uk
To: Patricia Ryan, P.Ryan@bigplace.com
Subject: **Hello (2)**

Pat,

\>> MEMO TO SELF:
THE PASTOR IS NOT IN CHARGE.

I don't know about you, but I always thought that the minister or vicar ran the church. Or failing that, the PCC or diaconate or whoever. But no. The person who really runs things is the caretaker.

I met ours earlier. His name is Stanley. At first glance he looked OK. A retired gent, always been in the church, gave me a nice smile and said 'hello'.

'Hi,' I said. 'I'm Chris.'

'And what do you do, Chris?' he asked.

'Oh,' I replied. 'I'm sorry, I thought you knew. I'm the new youthworker.'

Immediately something changed. The temperature dropped about twenty degrees and there was a long, uncomfortable silence, the kind where you can hear the wind quietly moaning in the trees. I half expected a ball of tumbleweed to come blowing through the church. The smile on his face was snapped shut and put away in its box.

'I don't want this place left in a tip,' he said, tight-lipped. 'My mother came here all her life.'

I couldn't quite see the link between these two statements, but I thought I'd better pacify him all the same. 'Of course not,' I replied. 'I'll make sure it's all clean.'

'Good. Just as long as we know where we stand.'

Somehow, I didn't feel this was the best start to our relationship.

'I was just checking,' I said, 'I'm thinking of starting a new Tuesday night group. Is the hall available?'

He looked at me like I'd suggested we organise a conga on his mother's grave.

'Tuesdays?' he replied. 'That's the ladies' fellowship night. We have a big ladies' fellowship here.'

'Where do the small ladies go?' I asked. The smile didn't return.

'It isn't available,' he said.

'Well, how about Wednesday?'

'You'll have to talk to the pastor,' he said, without answering the question. 'He'll no doubt have an opinion on the idea.'

I had a nasty suspicion that, at the earliest opportunity, he would tell the pastor exactly what opinion he should have of the idea. So, not exactly an auspicious start to our relationship. So I thought I'd cheer myself up by checking out the equipment. The cupboard was locked. So I had to troop back to find Stanley and ask for a key.

'You'll have to ask the pastor,' he repeated. 'I can't just give you anything you need.'

I have the feeling this statement is going to define our relationship.

In the end I managed to persuade him to open the cupboard for me. To call it a disappointment would be far too cheerful a view. Our 'well-stocked youth resources' consist of:

- 3 table tennis bats with the rubber peeling off
- 1 game of Twister without the bit you spin round
- 1 dog-eared copy of *101 Epilogues for Desperate Youth Leaders*
- An empty plastic box marked 'Tuck Shop'
- 1 pool table propped up on a pile of old hymn-books as it only has three legs

- A battered stereo system with only one speaker
- A black and white television (not working)
- Some wax crayons
- A copy of *Smash Hits*, dated 21 April 1976

Tonight I'm going to meet the youth group properly for the first time and then tomorrow I have a church leadership meeting. I will have to raise the issue of a budget. Urgently.

On my way out of the church there was a kid sitting on the church steps. Well, I say 'kid'. It was actually a three-foot high cave-dweller, who was managing to eat chips despite having a fag-end surgically attached to his lower lip. I tried to talk to him but he just glared at me. It put me in mind of those late-night conversations we had at college – how we were going to take the gospel to the kids, how we were going to change the face of Christian youthwork.

Well, I have seen the face of youthwork. It was scoffing chips and wearing a fag.

Cheers
Chris

From: Chris Francis@Tabernacle.ch.uk
To: Patricia Ryan, P.Ryan@bigplace.com
Subject: Youth group

Pat,

OK. I've just met the youth group.

I followed that up by taking some Paracetamol.

This is not a youth group; it's a therapy class. Let me just sketch in some of the people.

Vanessa is fifteen, blonde and held my hand for just slightly too long when she shook it. I'm going to have to watch that one. Glenda was wearing army fatigues and about three million badges, mostly related to the environment. She looked at my leather jacket and just said 'Animal murderer.' Andy has been coming to the church for a few months. He is an apprentice at the local garage. He seems OK. Just a bit quiet.

Among the younger kids we have Giles, a small lad in the group who wouldn't say boo to a goose but whose adherence to the more extreme forms of heavy metal was demonstrated by the fact that he was wearing a black T-shirt with the slogan 'Maximum Carnage to Your Ear Drums' on it. However, as he was also wearing corduroy trousers and a pair of highly-polished brogues I didn't think he'd entirely bought into the world of heavy rock. Then there is Aruna, a young girl who looked at me as though she was weighing me up and asked me frighteningly intelligent questions about the sociological background of my approach to youthwork.

And there's Julian. Julian was wearing a cagoule and thick glasses. His hair was so greasy you could oil your engine with his head. I introduced myself to him. He peered at me intently for a second and then demanded: 'Are you washed in the blood of the Lamb?'

I replied, 'No, it's Imperial Leather actually.'

>> MEMO TO SELF:
   DO NOT, UNDER ANY CIRCUMSTANCES TRY TO JOKE WITH
   JULIAN.

It took another 20 minutes to convince him that I actually was a Christian, that I wasn't just posing as a youth leader in order to undermine the faith of the young people and that I didn't think personal salvation was a laughing matter. He then gave me a tract on personal holiness and a booklet about Revelation.

I thought I'd try a different tack and so I asked them about their ambitions. Glenda wants to save the whales; Giles wants to explore 'prophetic guitar distortion'; Aruna wants to be nuclear physicist; Vanessa wants to marry a nice Christian man (she looked at me strangely when she said this) and Julian wanted 'to be martyred for the faith'. Andy thought for a moment and then said, 'I want to change things.' He didn't really elaborate on what it was he wanted changed, it could have been carburettors for all I know, but there are obviously things that concern him.

I broached with them the idea of the Tuesday night open youth club and whether they wanted to come along. They didn't seem that keen, actually. Julian claimed he always had a half-night of prayer on Tuesdays, while Glenda said she had her hunt saboteur action group meeting. Vanessa just giggled. After they left, I was feeling a bit depressed when Andy came back.

'About Tuesdays,' he said. 'I'll help if you want.'

I was really delighted! I can see it's going to be a bit of an issue, integrating the unchurched kids with the Christians, but at least I have my first helper.

As if to emphasise this dilemma, the kid with the fag was sitting on the steps again tonight. I don't know how to approach him. What can I do to make contact? Where can I find out about him? Any advice you have to give would be appreciated.

Other than that, everything is well.

Cheers
Chris

From: Chris Francis@Tabernacle.ch.uk
To: Patricia Ryan, P.Ryan@bigplace.com
Subject: The leadership team

Pat,

Thanks for your email. It's early days at the moment, so there is a lot to tell you about.

Like last night's meeting of the church leadership team.

I'd met them before, of course, but that was at the interview, when they were keen for me to take on the job. Now they've 'got me' I had the feeling that the dynamic had changed slightly. The meeting was interesting. Those physically present were the pastor, myself, and the elders. But I also got the distinct impression that the spirit of Stanley was inhabiting the place, hovering over proceedings like some kind of malignant ghost.

I asked about a set of keys. Pastor told me to ask Stanley. I said that Stanley had told me to ask him. In the end one of the elders gave me his set so I could make copies. I had to promise not to tell Stanley. I asked about a budget for the youthwork. I was told the deacons would have to approve it. When I told them the figure I had in mind there was a sort of silence around the room.

'But, these are just children,' said Dennis. (He's the treasurer, and he and Cecily are the elders. Although unrelated, I suspect them to be the outcome of some early cloning experiment.) 'Do we really need to spend that much?'

'Yes we do,' I replied. And I outlined my plans for the new Tuesday night club. They were very keen to make contact with unchurched kids.

'As long as you don't forget your primary responsibility is to the children already in the church,' said the pastor.

'That's not what I came here to do,' I pointed out. 'We agreed that my primary role was to bring new kids in.'

'Yes, well, perhaps you'll have to concentrate on both.'

'I thought you were here to run the Sunday school,' suggested Cecily.

We appear to be suffering from what is technically known as 'Role Confusion'. I decided not to pursue the matter there and then, but to bring my job description to the next meeting. 'But,' I said, 'we've got a problem about Tuesdays, because of the ladies' fellowship.'

'Oh, don't worry about that,' said the pastor. 'As far as I know only three women go. They can hold it in the small meeting room.' I told him what Stanley had said. It transpires that Stanley's mother had started the ladies' fellowship in 1926. Something tells me we could be in for a struggle here.

Cheers
Chris

From: Chris Francis@Tabernacle.ch.uk
To: Patricia Ryan, P.Ryan@bigplace.com
Subject: Youth group

Pat,

On Sunday morning the pastor stood up and said, 'As the children leave us for their own activities, the congregation will stand and sing "Give Thanks with a Grateful Heart".'

I don't think he spotted the irony of his words, but as I stood up I wondered if it was a sign. I was going to do an appeal for more people to help with the youthwork. We need people to help out at virtually every level, so I gave an eloquent and impassioned call for new blood. I poured my heart and soul into my presentation; I spoke of the fact that young people were vital for any growing church, that there was a huge mission field just waiting for people to get involved, that it was a challenging, but fun thing to do.

The effect was remarkable. You could almost grab a handful of air and squeeze the apathy out of it. One or two church members were so moved they almost woke up.

After the service, I stood waiting for the helpers to rush into my arms. Julian approached me but luckily it was only to give me a tract entitled 'Revival – Are You a Blockage?' If he carries on giving me leaflets at the rate he is I'm going to need to build some bigger bookshelves. Then Stanley, the caretaker came up to me.

'Your youth group used up all the toilet paper,' he said.

'And a very good morning to you,' I replied.

'You may not think it's a serious issue,' he continued. 'But paper doesn't grow on trees, you know.'

I was about to point out that strictly speaking, this wasn't true, but I couldn't be bothered.

At the end, when everyone had gone, the pastor came over.

'Don't be dispirited,' he said.

'I'm sorry,' I replied. 'It's just I hoped to be able to start building a team.'

'Oh, it's always been the same here,' he continued. 'We've never been able to get people to do the youthwork. That's why we employed you.'

Somehow I didn't find this comforting. But he's right. One of the key reasons that churches employ a youthworker is so that they don't have to do the job themselves.

'Maybe I'll have to try a different tack,' I said. 'Like kidnapping the organist.'

'That's a good idea,' said the pastor. 'And if they don't sign up for your team you could threaten to give him back.'

I went home to the traditional youthworker's Sunday lunch (pizza) and began to feel a failure. My flat felt cold and lonely. Anyway, a little while after that there was a knock on the door and Andy arrived. You remember him? Works at the garage. He'd come round to talk about the Tuesday group. He suggested – actually I should shout this – HE SUGGESTED WE PRAY.

So we started to pray and then the phone rang. I almost didn't answer it, but I'd forgotten to put the answerphone on, so I picked the thing up. It was a church member called Julie. She offered to help with the youthwork.

I gave thanks with a grateful heart. I'm just grateful that God doesn't take Sundays off.

Of course, now I need to think about team building and more recruitment and leadership meetings and all that...

Cheers
Chris

From: Chris Francis@Tabernacle.ch.uk
To: Patricia Ryan, P.Ryan@bigplace.com
Subject: Youth group budgets

Hi Pat,

Thanks for the advice about the budgets. And you're right about the need for prayer. In fact, I've organised a weekly prayer meeting especially for the young people and the youthwork. Attendees so far included myself, Julie and Julian (the trainee martyr).

Julie is a bit of a gem. She's a teacher at the local primary school, so her getting involved in youthwork is beyond the call of duty. Anyway, we only got in a prayer each before Julian started praying. And praying. And praying.

After 42 minutes, Julie and I slipped out and made a coffee, returning just in time for a final blessing, a quote from Leviticus and a resounding 'Amen'. I don't think he noticed. He seemed quite happy and he left me a tract entitled 'How to Pray for the Spiritually Dead'.

I'm still working on the Tuesday night group, so the advice about approaching local businesses is particularly helpful. I'm going to meet the caretaker tomorrow to sort a few issues out. I don't know about prayer warriors... I think I could do with the assistance of a couple of Samurai warriors.

Cheers
Chris

From: Chris Francis@Tabernacle.ch.uk
To: Patricia Ryan, P.Ryan@bigplace.com
Subject: The great peace negotiations

Pat,

I went to Stanley – the caretaker's – house this evening for a meeting about what he called 'certain issues'. To say that I was dreading this would be an understatement. But I really needed to get things sorted.

Stanley was in the front garden when I arrived. He was vacuuming the lawn.

'Hello,' I said.

'Don't walk on the grass,' he replied. I basked in the glow of this warm reception. 'We'll have to make this quick,' he added, 'only I don't want to miss the shipping forecast.'

I smiled my best smile. You know, the one that says, 'I'm a warm, caring individual and I really want to bond with you.' The one that all youthworkers have to master at an early stage.

'I suppose you'll be wanting a cup of tea,' he sniffed. And with that we trooped inside.

It's difficult to describe the inside of his house. The living room is dominated by photos of his mother, Marjorie. There are photos on the mantelpiece, photos on the tables, even paintings on the wall. It's a kind of shrine. It's the Marj Mahal.

All of which wouldn't have mattered so much had his mother been at all photogenic. Sadly, she looked like Winston Churchill's bigger sister. Or possibly his brother, in drag.

Even so, there was something about one of the photos that struck me. There she was, surrounded, engulfed, by kids. This was several decades ago, when Sunday school outings were organised along the lines of military campaigns – you know, full dress uniform, synchronise watches, anyone found eating their sandwiches early will be shot – but even so, she positively glowed. She looked *almost* attractive.

'Bournemouth, 1948,' said Stanley, arriving with the tea. 'It rained.'

He took the photo frame out of my hand, gave it a quick polish where I'd obviously got my fingerprints on it, and replaced it on the shelf.

'Who are they all?'

'Sunday school outing. Mother was in charge of the Sunday school, for about forty years.'

I looked at the picture. 'I think they loved her,' I said.

Suddenly we had another atmosphere shift. It was like the air after a storm; all that tension, all the electricity that had crackled between us just seemed to evaporate.

'Yes,' said Stanley. 'They did.'

He began to tell me the story. She had virtually kept the church going in the forties and fifties – Sunday school superintendent, organising the women's group, church secretary, if there was a job that needed doing, she did it. Most surprising of all, she organised several missions in the town and even set up an early drop-in centre for the young unemployed.

'She sounds a remarkable woman,' I said.

'She was,' he replied. 'Not that she ever got thanks for it.'

Sensing we were about to move back to the familiar ground of tight-lipped tenseness, I started to talk about the plans I had – the Tuesday night group.

'Look, I don't mean to be difficult, but who has to clean up all this?' he demanded. 'You have the good ideas, but who's left with the mess? Do you know what happens after every church service? I have to go around clearing up notice sheets that people just throw down. I wouldn't mind if it was just negligence, but it's worse than that. It's disdain. It's the thought that "someone else will do it". I've lost count of the number of sermons I've heard in my life on servanthood, but it's the old story. Everyone wants to preach on it, but no one wants to do it.'

Suddenly I had a vision of what his life must be like. It wasn't that he didn't care; it was that others didn't care about him.

'All right,' I said. 'We'll make a deal. I will be personally responsible for the room. No – better than that – the young people will be responsible for the room. We will decorate it, and we will clean it. I don't want to be a burden to anybody.'

There was a pause.

'But what about the ladies' fellowship?' he said. 'They use the room.'

'There are only three of them. They can go in the Manse.' I pointed at the photo. 'I know your mother started it, but all I want to do is do what she did – give young people somewhere to go, somewhere to belong. Don't you think that she would have preferred that?'

Stanley looked at me. For a moment I thought he was going to smile.

'It's a deal,' he said.

It was only as I shut his front gate behind me that I realised I had committed the youth group to cleaning up after them. Somehow I think the battle has only just begun.

Cheers

Chris

From: Chris Francis@Tabernacle.ch.uk
To: Patricia Ryan, P.Ryan@bigplace.com

Subject: Tuesday nights

Hi Pat,

Tuesday nights begin tonight! (Or rather the Tuesday night youth club.)

Andy and I have worked hard at converting the room – we've created a 'bar' area for tuck, drinks, handing in your offensive weapons, etc. We were halfway through this, bits of wood flying everywhere, when Stanley walked in.

'What are you doing?' he asked.

My heart stopped. 'Here we go,' I thought. Confrontation. The final showdown. Hold the front page – 'Youthworker Beats Caretaker to Death with a Claw Hammer'.

'We're building a bar,' said Andy before I could stop him and claim that we were doing something more spiritual, like creating a two-storey baptistry or something.

'No,' said Stanley. 'I mean, you're not doing it right. If you drill it that way it's going to be a right mess.'

And there and then he mucked in and completed the thing. Admittedly after we'd finished he gave me a lecture on the state of the toilet floor after Sunday night, but it was a bit half-hearted and I got the distinct impression he was only lecturing me out of habit.

This project is creating all kinds of ripples in the church. I was down there yesterday – pathetically trying to stick the rubber back on a table tennis bat using some sellotape and a bit of Blu-Tack – when the pastor suddenly materialised out of nowhere. He seems to have this knack of appearing and disappearing without you noticing it. Pastors are like policemen – there's never one around when you need them.

'I want to talk to you about something,' he said, in that 'prepare-yourself-for-half-an-hour-of-character-assassination' voice that only Christians seem to possess. 'A number of church members are a bit worried about all this.'

'All what?' I asked.

'Well, this new initiative. I mean, don't think that we're not in favour, of course we are. But you must make sure that you're not being deflected from your primary task.'

'Which is?'

'Pastoring the progeny of the flock.'

I must have looked blank.

'Working with the sons and daughters of church members.'

'I thought my primary role is to reach out to new kids,' I said.

'I don't think so,' said the pastor. 'I think you'll find that it is to maintain and develop the present youth structures. That's what it says in the job description.'

'Exactly. Develop. I'm developing. I'm trying to do something new, something important.'

We stared at each other for a moment.

'Chris,' he smiled. 'It's not a big issue. More a "concern". I mean, don't think I'm not supportive of this. I'm right behind you.'

Yes, I thought. With a knife to stab in my back.

'I didn't want there to be any misunderstanding,' he continued. 'Just as long as we understand each other.'

And with that he left.

Understand? As far as I was concerned he could have been talking fluent Assyrian. What is going on here? This isn't the first time I've encountered this kind of thinking. I'm trying to reach out to people who normally wouldn't enter a church. I thought that's what we were supposed to do, but it's almost as if people are scared of this – or of what it will mean for the church.

So much for the church sharing my vision.

I'm probably being too hard on him. I'm sure he wants this initiative to succeed. It was just a bit discouraging. So anyway, what do I do? Do I concentrate on the church kids, or on the unchurched kids? And how can I deal with this misconception? I am committed to the church kids, but I can't just leave it at that, can I? Please write.

Cheers
Chris

PS: Just the one tract from Julian this week: 'Personal Spirituality and Footwear – The Call to Sandals'.

From: Chris Francis@Tabernacle.ch.uk
To: Patricia Ryan, P.Ryan@bigplace.com
Subject: First Tuesday

Dear Pat,

Well, to paraphrase that great youthworker, Julius Caesar, 'We came, we saw, we just about survived.' Last night was the first open youth group. I think it will help you if I break it down into timings.

19:00 Final preparations. Prayer with Julie and Andy. Julian arrives halfway through. I didn't know he was coming, but he can smell a prayer meeting up to half a mile away. He's like an evangelical sniffer dog.

19:45 Discover Julian is laying out tracts. Each table has several copies of 'Are You Damned to Eternal Torment?' by someone called Rev Murdo McBrightly. Surreptitiously remove them.

19:52 Andy informs me that of the two pool cues we have, one is only seven inches long and the other has no tip. I hurriedly scribble a notice announcing our new Pool Hustler's Challenge. 'Now we've made pool even more challenging!' screams the sign. Discover a tract entitled '666 In the Top Pocket – The Godlessness of Pool, Snooker and Bar Billiards' hidden under the scoreboard. Remove it.

20:00 Doors open. No one enters. No one is even waiting. I AM IN DESPAIR. I am the worst youthworker in the history of humankind. Andy and Julie seem quite relaxed.

20:04 About seven young people enter – all kids I saw while taking part in a lesson in school last week. I AM IN ECSTASY. Begin drafting my seminar for trainee youthworkers on 'Reaching the Unchurched and Building a Mighty Army for God'.

20:06   Two of them leave after seeing the pool cues. I AM RELAXED. My pulse is more even now and I have stopped hyperventilating.

20:10   Some of the church kids arrive. Vanessa rushes up to me and flings her arms around me. 'You're so wonderful!' she breathes. I tell her to go and check the ladies loos. She comes back with a copy of 'Women – God's Chosen Handmaidens' – a tract she found tucked into the toilet-roll holder. In a panic I check the gents. I just manage to flush a copy of 'Tight Jeans and the Path of Lust' down the toilet before anyone gets to it.

20:30   onwards. The rest of the evening went by in a whirl. The music was good, the atmosphere was great, the pool cues need replacing. Both Andy and Julie said they had some good conversations and we had about thirteen kids in all. Not bad for a start. I even stopped shaking about halfway through.

There were some issues, of course. I discovered that someone had locked Julian in the broom cupboard at one stage ('I was only challenging his personal spirituality,' he claimed) and the church kids didn't mix with the unchurched kids at all. But overall I'm very pleased. Julian was ecstatic because all his tracts had been taken. I don't think he approved of my 'no epilogue' policy however. How was I going to get the message across? he asked. I hadn't really thought about that. Any ideas?

Cheers
Chris

From: Chris Francis@Tabernacle.ch.uk
To: Patricia Ryan, P.Ryan@bigplace.com
Subject: Update

Hi Pat,

It was great to see you the other day, even if it was only for a flying visit. I'm glad things are going well with you.

Something has been bothering me about Julian for a while, but I've not been able to put my finger on it. I mean, I know he has the kind of religious fanaticism that makes the Spanish Inquisition seem a bit half-hearted, but there was more to it than that.

So I went round to his house on a Thursday night. I knew he would be in because it's the only night we don't have any church meetings.

The door was opened by his mother. I don't know what I was expecting. Maybe a short woman with jam-jar glasses and dressed in all-black. Or possibly a nun. But Julian's mother is a striking woman in her forties. I suppose 'elegant' is the only word to describe her.

'Hello,' she said, after I'd introduced myself. 'Come in. Julian's told me a lot about you.'

'Oh,' I replied. 'I hope it was all good.'

'To be honest I didn't understand a lot of it,' she confided. 'And anyway, I've no idea what a "neo-liberal heretic" is.'

We chatted a bit and it transpired that she works as a PA for a firm of solicitors in the town.

'What does your husband do?' I asked.

She looked startled. 'Don't you know?'

'Know what?'

'My husband died three years ago. I'm surprised Julian hasn't told you.'

It was one of those moments when you realise that you've found out something very important, and at the same time you wish the floor would open up and swallow you.

'No,' I mumbled. 'I didn't know that. Sorry.'

'It's all right,' she said. 'It was cancer. There was nothing anyone could do.' She looked at me. 'I think the church has been a real help to Julian. Sometimes I worry that it's taking him over a bit, but, well, when all the stuff with his father happened, I think it sort of kept him together.' She smiled. 'Anyway, you came to see Julian. I'll take you up.'

We went upstairs. From a door on the left there came the unmistakable sound of a Graham Kendrick tape. She knocked on the door and a startled-looking Julian invited me in.

How do I describe his room? Well, if you took an average-sized Christian bookshop and put a bed and two chairs in it, you'd just about be there. From floor to ceiling the walls were lined with books on every Christian topic.

'Wow,' I said. 'Have you read all these?'

'Oh no,' he replied. He pointed into the corner. 'There are at least three I haven't got round to yet.'

I looked at the books again. So many books on living the victorious life, mastering the doctrine, understanding the spiritual forces... and down in one corner, tucked away on a bottom shelf, a slim white book, and written on its spine: *Living With Loss*. All these books, just papering over the cracks.

We sat and talked for a while.

'I hope you didn't mind me coming to see you,' I said. 'You know, I was just passing.'

He blinked at me, owlishly, from behind his big glasses. I don't think either of us was fooled.

'I don't mind,' he said. 'I don't get many visitors. I tend to spend a lot of my time reading... or praying... or both.'

'Your mum told me about your dad,' I said. 'I'm really sorry about that.'

'It's OK,' he replied. 'I'm victorious over it.'

'That's good.' I nodded. 'That's good.' But he didn't look very victorious.

'Julian,' I said. 'I'm going to tell you something that no one else knows about – no one around here, at any rate.'

And I sat down and told him about Sarah and all the plans we had and the car accident and everything. I told him everything I felt about God at the time, and how I nearly let all the anger eat me alive. I wondered, as I told him, what he would say, how he would respond. I had a horrible feeling that this would be the nail in my coffin, the final straw, the proof he had been waiting for that I was not a real Christian leader at all; that I was just a fake.

'I still miss her,' I said, finally. 'I see her face, hear her voice. It's not wrong to be sad.'

He looked at me as though he had no idea what I was talking about. There was a sort of angry bewilderment that someone had peered into this small private place.

'I'm not sad,' he insisted. 'I've learnt how to give praise to God in every circumstance. I'm living in his will.'

'That's good,' I replied. 'I just wanted you to know. That's all.'

I felt small, foolish. So we chatted about some other things and then I left.

The next day I went out to do an assembly at the local school, then met with the pastor for lunch and then headed home. When I got there I noticed that an envelope had dropped on my doormat with 'To the Youth Minister' written on it. I knew it was from Julian. Apart from the fact that he has, apparently, developed a handwriting style based on ancient Aramaic, he's the only person alive who still uses the term 'Youth Minister'.

I opened it, expecting to find a tract on 'Christian Optimism' or 'The Victory of the True Believer' but instead I found a letter. No, not a letter: two words.

'Thank you.'

Cheers
Chris

teething troubles

From: Chris Francis@Tabernacle.ch.uk

To: Patricia Ryan, P.Ryan@bigplace.com

Subject: Druids

Pat,

I opened my Bible today and read Proverbs 22:6 – 'Train a child in the way he should go, and when he is old he will not turn from it.' Obviously the writer of Proverbs was not a church youthworker.

I had coffee with Glenda, one of my youth group. I like Glenda. She's very intelligent, passionate about the environment, and wears clothes that look like they've been in a war (why is it that so many peace activists wear army surplus gear? Am I missing some irony here? Or is it just cheap?).

More significantly, Glenda has a boyfriend, Sven. I've only met him once as he spends most of his time underground, protesting against road building. But he is clearly exerting a powerful influence.

'I need your help,' she said.

'About what?' I asked.

'Druids.' There was a moment's silence.

'Druids?'

'Yes, Sven is a druid.'

'Let me get this clear,' I said, starting to grin, 'you're going out with a subterranean, Norwegian druid?'

'I don't see anything funny in that,' said Glenda.

'No. Of course not.'

'Anyway, my mum and dad keep lecturing me about going out with nice Christian boys and all that. But I love Sven.' She looked at me. 'He wants us to live together. In a tunnel under the new runway extension at Stansted airport.'

'I see.'

'So what should I do?' she asked.

'Well for one thing, if he carries you over the threshold I would duck.'

'That's not very funny,' she said.

'No, no, I'm sorry.' I stared at my coffee for a moment.

'Well?' she demanded.

'First,' I ventured, 'I would start thinking for myself.'

'What do you mean?'

'Well, it's not about what your parents think or what I think, or even what Sven thinks. It's between you and God. It's not my job to take over the running of your life. I'm your youth leader, not your personal decision-maker. It's your decision. It's about who you are going to put in charge of your life. It's about whether Jesus is really in charge of your life, or not.'

'You know he is... I think he is.' Her head drooped. 'Oh, I don't know. How can I?'

'It's hard,' I agreed. 'But someone very wise once said to me that you will never know if Christ is in charge, until you want to go one way, and he wants you to go in the other direction, and you choose his way.'

She looked up, almost angry. 'But that's so narrow!'

'It's not meant to be.'

'Don't you understand what you are doing?' she asked. 'The facts are that there are not enough men in the church today. So if you tell all girls that they should only marry Christians, you are condemning others to remain unmarried. You are basically telling them to become nuns. It's OK for you, though, sitting there all smug, because you'll be all right. You're a bloke and you're bound to find some poor, desperate Christian girl. Easy pickings for men.'

There was a silence. I thought of Sarah and the dark night and the wreckage of the car. Just like I've thought of her every day since. For a fleeting moment I wanted to shout at this girl, to tell her that we'd all suffered, that she had no monopoly on pain. But I knew that I couldn't give in to that luxury.

'It's not necessarily easy for us, either,' I said. 'But the truth is the truth. Only you know what you must do. You've heard the teaching. You know all the arguments. It's your choice.'

She looked down. Her hands twisted in her lap. I realised she was crying.

'Somebody is responsible for this!' she sobbed. 'I mean, I want to do what's right. But look at the church. It's dead. It's lifeless. People like Sven, they dismiss us as irrelevant. And he's right.'

'You're being a bit harsh.'

'Am I?' She dabbed her eyes with a paper napkin. 'I brought Sven to church once. I told him it would be relevant and interesting. We had four hymns, a prayer for missionaries in Guatemala and a sermon on the Eschatological Vision of Ezekiel.'

Despite herself, despite the tears, she started laughing.

'It's not funny,' she half-sobbed, half-chuckled. 'It's not funny! It's tragic.' She looked up. Her mascara had run down her face making her look like a terminally-ill panda. 'Don't you see?' she whispered. 'The church failed me. Why should I have to be punished because of the failure of others?'

I didn't say anything. What could I say? So much of what she says is right. I know all the theory, I know all the arguments, but what do I say?

So in the end I just repeated what I'd said earlier. But it was a real lesson for me. You see, you learn all the theory in college, don't you? You mug up on all the dogma and the doctrine – you even do exams in the stuff. But you never think about the impact these doctrines have on real people. There ought to be a module in all theology courses on 'What doctrine really means in practice'. It's the theological equivalent of the butterfly effect: some theologian somewhere interprets a line in Paul in a particular way and hundreds of years later, on the other side of the world, I end up sitting in a coffee bar watching a young girl cry her eyes out.

'You will never know whether Jesus is truly your Lord until you want to go one way, and he wants you to go another, and you choose his way.' That's what you told me all those years ago, when I was on the verge of quitting, when I wanted to throw it all away.

Well I went his way then, and I went his way today.

I just wish it felt more like a victory.

Cheers
Chris

From: Chris Francis@Tabernacle.ch.uk
To: Patricia Ryan, P.Ryan@bigplace.com
Subject: Spiritual thermometers

Pat,

Thanks for the inquiry. And thanks for the consoling words.

Yes, things are better now and yes I'm still talking to Glenda and no she hasn't made any decisions yet.

But it has made me think. Because, you know, all these things are going on in peoples' lives. Oh, you pick up on a lot; people tell you things and even a clinically-insensitive soul like myself can spot some things. But then there are a load of hidden factors at play. Like I had an email from the daughter of a friend of mine who said 'loads of my friends are backsliding. But not openly, so no one, except us, knows what is going on.'

Obviously I encouraged her and I'll continue to do so. But it did make me think. Because the real issue is, how do you take someone's spiritual temperature? How do you know someone's state of mind? Oh, it's fine with some people. I mean, if Julian prays for less than 45 minutes you know that he's backsliding. But with some of the others...

Of course it's great when the unlikely ones come up trumps. Andy, who most of the time gives the impression that he would rather have his teeth pulled than read the Bible, has actually suggested we start a 'Just Looking' group linked into the Tuesday nights.

He has offered to lead it, as he says this will be 'less threatening'! I feel like the Godfather, but he's probably right and he's been a fantastic help with all the work so far. The slight worry is that I don't know whether he should be leading a group. Once again I don't really know the extent of his knowledge. I don't want to police him, but how do I know if he's got the ability to run the group? How do I know if he'll be able to answer the questions?

I don't want to stifle his enthusiasm, but nor do I want to create a small group of heretics in the church. 'Looking' is great, but someone needs to be able to help with the 'finding'. When it comes to dismantling a Ford he's brilliant; when it comes to explaining the resurrection I have my doubts. Any advice?

Other than that, Tuesday nights are going well.

Julian came in last night wearing a sandwich board which proclaimed 'The End of the World is Nigh'. I told him that if he continued to wear it the end of his world would be very nigh indeed. He took it off, and today I had a tract through my door entitled 'The Big Spit is Coming – A Warning to Lukewarm Christians from Revelation.' Still, his heart's in the right place... shame about his brain.

Cheers
Chris

PS: I know I failed my church doctrine paper four times at college. That's not the point...

From: Chris Francis@Tabernacle.ch.uk
To: Patricia Ryan, P.Ryan@bigplace.com
Subject: How do I close my open door?

Pat,

When I was young, I used to spend loads of my time round at your house, didn't I? You had an open-door policy. In all that time that I used to hang around, I never recall you saying the words, 'Go away and leave me in peace, you annoyingly spotty little baboon.'

Now I am a grown up and mature youthworker (well grown up, anyway), I am starting to realise the truth. There must have been many times when every fibre of your being cried out to utter those words, when all you wanted was to be left alone...

Take tonight for instance.

It began at 3:30 p.m., when Vanessa called round on her way back from school to 'share with me a particularly beautiful passage from the Song of Solomon'. I can't quite recall the section – I think it had something to do with antelopes – but I'd just made her a coffee and rejected, for the fifteenth time, her offer to darn my socks, do my washing and run me up some new curtains, when, mercifully, the doorbell rang.

4:15 p.m., enter Glenda, in tears. Another fight with Sven. Sven is no longer, I am glad to say, an underground druid, but has moved on to embrace Zoroastrianism and start his own organic bean farm. (I saw him the other day. He's also embraced body piercing. His face has so many bits of metal in it, it takes him all the strength he can muster to nod his head. I hope he never tries to get on an aircraft; the metal-detector would explode. Nice bloke, though. I have hopes...)

Anyway, after I'd done the normal pastoral bit with Glenda and calmed her down and told her for the umpteenth time that she has to come to a decision about this one, it was 5:30 and I made some toast. At which point Andy arrived with the publicity for the Just Looking group. Or 'Just Looking grope' as it appears on his computer-generated leaflets.

'I did spell check it,' he said.

'Andy,' I said, 'we can't hand these out. It will send out all the wrong signals.'

'You're right,' he said. 'Mind you, we'd get loads of lads along, wouldn't we?'

So he trudged off to re-do it on his mate's computer. But not before consuming four rounds of toast, half a packet of Hobnobs and an apple.

By 6:45, Glenda had recovered her poise and was going through my kitchen cupboards, sorting everything into 'vegan', 'additive-infected' and 'blood-stained carnivore' piles.

'I won't throw it out for you,' she said. 'Your conscience must be your guide.'

'Actually, my stomach is my guide,' I replied, eyeing the steak and kidney pudding that she'd discovered at the back of the cupboard.

'Animal murderer.'

7:30. Glenda and Vanessa were just heading off, when Julian arrived. (Or, perhaps, because Julian arrived.) He handed me a copy of his latest acquisition, 'Are You Looking at Your End?' This illuminating look at death, written by the prolific Rev Murdo McBrightly was mainly printed in large red letters and underlined.

By the time we'd finished discussing this deathless piece of evangelistic prose, Andy was back with the revamped publicity.

'Do you think people will come to a "Just Locking group", Andy?' I asked.

'Oh %!**%@!' he said.

Julian covered his ears, muttered a prayer, whipped the tract from my hand and gave it to Andy.

'You have an impure tongue,' he said.

'No, I %!**%@ing don't!' replied Andy.

We then had a spirited discussion on swearing, personal integrity, qualifications for Christian leadership and being relevant to contemporary society.

At 8:40 some of the other young people dropped in, who 'just happened to be passing', the coffee flowed and I thought, wistfully, of my steak and kidney pudding.

I eventually ate at 11:30. I was only interrupted by three phone calls.

And this was a quiet night.

I believe in open house. I am delighted that they feel they can just drop in. I know that relational youthwork is the key to it all. But I'm falling apart at the seams. How do I stop hospitality turning into hostility? Answers please.

Cheers
Chris

PS: The new publicity arrived from Andy this morning. Apparently we're running a 'Rust Looking grape'. I can't wait.

From: Chris Francis@Tabernacle.ch.uk
To: Patricia Ryan, P.Ryan@bigplace.com
Subject: Alternative worship

Hi Pat,

Thanks for your comments on the state of things. It's great to have your encouragement. Tuesday nights have settled down really well. There is a good buzz going and we're starting to attract a good core of 'regulars'.

There is a real interest in spiritual things – something which I found surprising. We hear so much about the apathy of young people and the 'post-Christian generation' you'd think they weren't interested at all.

If anything, the kids I speak to are interested in too much. For them, Christianity is mixed in with astrology, Feng Shui and alien abductions. Unravelling all this presents a major challenge. I mean, you and I know that Christianity is qualitatively different from horoscopes and Feng Shui and crystals and all that. But distinguishing Christian spirituality from a lot of the New Age baggage will not be easy.

(Speaking of New Age baggage, the good news is that Sven the Underground Zoroastrian has been making infrequent appearances.

He's a nice guy – if a bit muddy. He couldn't stay for long – they work a strict rota system down the tunnels and it was his turn to do the tea.)

So anyway, I want to tap into this spirituality, to start where these kids are. But I don't want to appear to be agreeing with, or condoning, some of their ideas. I want to start with a dialogue, which is not made any easier by Julian, who tends to launch into a deliverance ministry at the drop of a hat. I've had to ban him from discussions of this sort.

Another idea I had was to start a more accessible alternative Sunday service. I suppose it's alternative worship I'm after – although I have to admit that in my experience a lot of alternative worship is just regular worship with the volume turned up. I started to brainstorm ideas with the youth group.

'Why don't we hold a Luis Palau tribute evening?' suggested Julian. 'We could have readings from his books and video clips. It's a service with everything.'

'Except, perhaps, a congregation,' I replied.

'How about a pyjama service?' suggested Vanessa.

'A pyjama service?'

'Yes, everyone comes wearing pyjamas... or nighties.'

I hurriedly changed the subject.

'I think we should have a green service,' said Glenda. 'You know, where we can get in touch with the environment.' She paused for a moment and tears came to her eyes. 'We should all feel the pain of Wales.'

'What pain is that, then?' I asked. 'I mean, I know that a lot of the collieries have closed...'

'She means whales,' explained Vanessa. 'You lovely, silly man...'

'This church needs to be awake to recycling!' shouted Glenda.

'Well, the pastor recycles a lot of his sermon illustrations,' I answered. 'But how do we make it accessible to non-Christians?'

They all looked blank.

'But it's a church service,' said Vanessa. 'I didn't think they were supposed to be accessible. I mean, I can't even understand them myself, and I'm a Christian.'

We left the discussion there.

Have you any thoughts on the subject? Any ideas of an acceptable approach? Of course, all this pre-supposes that I'll be able to get the idea past the pastor and the elders.

All ideas welcomed with open arms.

Cheers
Chris

From: Chris Francis@Tabernacle.ch.uk
To: Patricia Ryan, P.Ryan@bigplace.com
Subject: The Youth Service

Pat,

You remember that we were planning an alternative service? Well, I spoke about it to the pastor who, to my astonishment, welcomed the project with open arms and said the youth should run it all. I was amazed. Until I noticed that he scheduled the whole thing in for one of his weekends off.

Anyway, I've been so busy with the Tuesday nights and some of my outreach work that I gave Andy specific responsibility to get a plan together. Due to my busy-ness and his complete-lack-of-organisational-skills-ness he didn't get back to me for ages. So it was only a few days before the event when he showed me what he called 'the Set List'.

I stared at it in horror. 'You've got Julian down to preach.'

'What's the problem?'

I stared at him. 'For a start the service is only supposed to be an hour long,' I said. 'Julian takes that long warming up. Secondly I want this to be a warm, welcoming service for non-Christian friends and parents. Not a meeting of the "You're all going to Hell Club".'

He smiled. 'It's cool,' he said. 'I've talked to him about it. He knows what's required.'

'No, no, no, this is Julian, we're talking about here. Mr Extreme.'

'You're being too hard. If you didn't want me to organise it, you shouldn't have asked.'

I looked at the piece of paper again.

'And what's this? Glenda is doing the prayers.'

'She's got lots of ideas. She's going to lead us all in what she calls a "primeval howl for the green places". I think it will be a laugh.'

'Prayers aren't supposed to be "a laugh"!'

'You know what I mean. It will be good.'

'Look, Andy,' I said, 'it's not your fault. I blame myself. I should have been more hands-on...'

'You don't trust me,' he blurted out at last. 'You've never properly trusted me.'

'I do.'

'No you don't. You're always checking up on me. Checking I've told people this and that. Checking what's happening in the Just Looking group. You won't relax about it.'

'It's not that,' I replied, despite the fact that it probably was that. 'It's just that I am responsible. If it goes pear-shaped then it's my head that's on the block.'

'You don't think I've thought about it.'

'I do.'

'Well let me do it my way, then. If it fails, it fails. You told me that you were here to help us grow and learn. That's what we're trying to do.'

'But...'

'If you want to take over, fine. But a lot of people have already put a lot of time into this. You'll have to explain to them.'

What could I do? I should have been more involved, I know, but he was right. I'd let him do it. I had to let him carry it through.

'All right,' I said. 'But please remember, for you it's just a youth service. For me it's a career...'

By Sunday evening I was shaking. I toyed with the idea running away, or of simulating illness. Then I thought that I would go, but that I'd wear a disguise, but the only disguise I had was a pair of Mickey Mouse ears and I thought that these would hardly make me look inconspicuous. So, in the end I crept in at the back and hid behind a pillar.

Vanessa opened the service with a time of worship. Giles was playing the music which meant that the volume was brain-numbingly high. I have never heard 'Reign in me' played as a thrash metal anthem before, but people seemed to be enjoying it. Then there was a heart-stopping moment as Vanessa announced her liturgical dance based around the parable of the wise and foolish virgins. Luckily, she got cramp halfway through, otherwise I shudder to think what might have happened.

Glenda's prayers proved to be remarkably restrained. Admittedly she accompanied them with a slideshow on the crimes of the fur industry, but at least there was a focus.

Then there was Julian. What can I say? He was... quiet. It was not a sermon, it was a... well, I guess 'reflection' is the right word. He was calm. He spoke with authority. He never once mentioned the Rev Murdo McBrightly (although he did say he had some leaflets to hand out at the end). In the middle of his talk he invited Andy up to give his testimony. I was amazed. There was lots more. A sketch, half-learnt. Some music played badly. A multi-media light show that consisted of switching on and off the OHP in time to the music. But somehow it all seemed to fit.

And the reaction was astonishing. There were parents there who were thrilled. And everyone was coming up to me and saying what a good job I'd done.

'But I didn't do anything,' I replied. 'They did it all.'

'That's probably why it was so good!' joked the treasurer.

And I knew he was right.

I wonder what it would have been like if I'd been involved. A lot slicker perhaps. A bit quieter maybe. But probably not as real.

Funny thing, delegation.

Cheers
Chris

From: Chris Francis@Tabernacle.ch.uk
To: Patricia Ryan, P.Ryan@bigplace.com
Re: Open house problems

Hi Pat,

Thanks for your response. Well, you may be right that running an open-door policy is harder if you're on your own. I've thought about sharing with someone else but there's a problem – the difficulty in finding suitable flatmates. I don't know why but I always have trouble finding the right sort. The last person I shared with was a guy called Gunter who had a blond moustache and played Matt Redman songs on his piano accordion at three o'clock in the morning.

Anyway, I appreciate the input and it does raise the interesting question of the whole 'singleness' thing. Just the other day, the pastor implied that, as I was single, I should be able to give more time than others to the work. The church seems to assume that I don't have a life outside of my job. I love it, but I also have a deep respect for what is left of my sanity.

And just as importantly as the workload of the so-called 'professionals', I've been trying to think through how much sacrifice we should expect from those who help us. Take Julie for example. Julie is quiet, efficient, great with the kids and very, very committed. She helps out on Tuesday and Sunday evenings, meets with me and Andy during the week to pray and plan, and holds down a job as a primary school teacher.

The other day she let slip to me that her husband, Dave, was getting a bit 'fed up' with her absences.

'He didn't mind the Tuesday nights,' she said, 'but it's the other things.'

The problem I have is that, without the other things, the Tuesday nights won't work as well. We need to meet and pray. But the last thing I want to do is cause friction between husband and wife, especially when they're such great people.

I wonder if you or any of your contacts have this kind of problem? Of course, it's not just a youthwork issue, although it seems to me that youthwork places uniquely stressful demands on people. The problem is that most employment is becoming ever more demanding... and so is the church. What kind of steps can we take to keep people involved, to use their skills and gifts, and at the same time avoid burning them out completely?

Cheers
Chris

From: Chris Francis@Tabernacle.ch.uk
To: Patricia Ryan, P.Ryan@bigplace.com
Subject: Terror, panic and despair...

Hi Pat,

Two words guaranteed to strike fear into the very heart of any church-based youthworker:

>> HOLIDAY CLUB

To most youthworkers these words cause the same feelings as the words 'black' and 'death' did to your average medieval peasant. The heart begins to pound, the blood rushes to your head, your limbs start to shake and the sky darkens with gloomy foreboding.

As you can tell, I am not a fan of this particular area of responsibility. I am writing this three days into Holiday Club, which, this year, has moved to the beginning of the summer holidays. It used to take place at the end of the summer holidays but, as one helper put it, 'it ruined my fortnight in Marbella, knowing I had that waiting for me when I returned.'

So we decided to bring it forward. Part of the reason for my trepidation about it was the age group: I don't normally associate with the seven to ten-year-olds.

There are, I am reliably informed, people who like working with this age group. But then again, there are people who enjoy potholing. There are even people who like the sound of bagpipes. No, give me teenagers any day. At least teenagers calm down occasionally. At least they stop moving (in fact we normally have the opposite problem. There is one lad in our group – Bernie – who has never actually been seen to move. It's a complete mystery as to how he arrives in meetings. He just seems to materialise.)

Anyway, back to the seven to ten-year-olds. I should have realised that things were not going to go smoothly when registration day came and we had 125 children. Our initial euphoria at the success of our poster campaign was tempered by the fact that the hall can only reasonably accommodate 45 and that Julian had promised all those who registered free Crunchies.

'I thought it would be an incentive,' he explained.

'Julian,' I pointed out, 'we have a budget for the week which is just enough to buy two pots of poster paint and some glitter. We don't have enough money for incentives.'

'Yes, but look at the number who came along!' he exclaimed.

'Yes, and look at the conditions,' I replied. 'We have 125 kids in that hall.'

Anyway, Julian made amends by going along to the garage and wheedling a load of Crunchies out of them by saying they were for a local youth project.

'The garage owner asked me if it was anything to do with the Prince's Trust,' he said, as he staggered back in with half a hundredweight of chocolate. 'I told him it was the Prince of Peace's Trust, and gave him a tract. I had just started to tell him about the apocalypse when he suddenly rushed out, found a box of chocolates and practically bundled me through the door.'

I also have a lot of concerns about the theme, as devised by Glenda and Esmerelda Van Sant, who leads the Sunday school. Call me Mr Boring, but 'Scrappy and his Friends at the Landfill Site' is not exactly obvious material. The whole thing is set in the local dump where 'Scrappy' (Esmerelda) lives along with her friends Neddy Newspaper (Glenda) Tommy Tin Can (Julian) and Betty Bottle (Aruna). Together they are learning about love, friendship and the importance of responsible waste disposal. However, their efforts at leading a good life are constantly undermined by Sammy the Sewer Rat (guess who), but don't worry, at the end of each day the rat gets thrown into the SEWER OF GUNGE!

Yes, at the end of each day a bunch of ten-year-olds get to cover me with gunge. Oh, how thigh-slappingly hilarious. I tell you, when you are facing a group of rabid, gunge-equipped ten-year-olds, it's enough to freeze the blood. Seeing the frenzy with which they set about their task gives you a whole new insight into the theory of evolution. It's like the Hitler Youth with buckets.

So, the upshot of this is that every morning at 8:30 I climb into my rat outfit and off I go for three hours of high-decibel mayhem. Three hours later I trudge home; tired, deaf and covered in papier-mâché, broken egg and wallpaper paste.

The fact that they're obviously having the time of their lives is no consolation.

Next year I am going to do Holiday Club totally differently. In 'Sammy the Sewer Rat's Ambient Chill-Out House' we will have cool worship, pina colladas for all the helpers and each day will end with Scrappy, Neddy Newspaper, Tommy Tin Can and Betty Bottle undergoing what I plan to call, 'The Great Recycling'.

And, of course, free Crunchies for all.

Cheers
Chris

youth
weekend

From: Chris Francis@Tabernacle.ch.uk

To: Patricia Ryan, P.Ryan@bigplace.com

Subject: Integration

Hi Pat,

The Tuesday night youth group meetings are now a well-established part of the youth strategy. They are mainly based on the simple, well-tried formula of giving young people a positive environment to look bored in. We do some activities and trips – a couple of weeks ago, for example, we all went to see a movie.

However, there is one thing we still haven't cracked: integration.

I just can't find a way to integrate the church and non-church kids together. It's not like they don't speak to one another, it's not like they don't know one another. But there's this barrier between them. And, increasingly, the church kids are reluctant to come on Tuesdays and the non-church kids have no intention of coming on Sunday nights.

There have, of course, been successes, but it's almost like once this happens, the person in question swaps from one tribe to the other. Former allegiances are dropped completely.

When we had a planning meeting last night I tried to raise the issue.

'It's been a few months now and I just think that we ought to be building bridges between the two groups,' I said.

'We have tried,' complained Vanessa. 'But the kids on Tuesdays don't want to know.'

'Speaking for myself,' said Julian. 'I believe God has called me to be a missionary to the pagans.' He lowered his eyes in humility. 'I believe that I am gradually gaining acceptance.'

Aruna snorted. 'Julian, everyone ignores you.'

'That is not true. Only the other night my message hit home with such prophetic power that I was almost martyred.'

'Well, not quite,' I said. 'Although I did have to restrain someone from beating you with a pool cue.'

'You see!' said Vanessa. 'That's exactly the kind of violent behaviour we expect from the Tuesday night crowd!'

'Um... no, it was someone at Sunday night's Bible study who tried to hit him,' I said.

'Oh. Still, they just don't mix with us.'

'But that's the whole point of Tuesdays!' I exclaimed. 'We're supposed to make links with them, to build bridges, to show how exciting church can be.'

There was a long pause.

'Which church is that, then?' asked Andy.

'Look, that's another issue. My point is, how do we integrate them into the wider church family?'

'Maybe,' suggested Vanessa, 'we could have a big party. You know, a social event... possibly with ballroom dancing.'

'Here's a radical suggestion,' said Julian. 'And, though I say it myself, possibly prophetic. We should declare a joint day of prayer and repentance. And fasting. And possibly offer a wave offering to the Lord as well. That's bound to bring total unity.'

'It will bring total unity,' said Glenda, 'because you'll be the only one doing it.' She paused. 'What about a joint project – you know, something practical we could all do together to help the community. We could organise something like a clean-up campaign for them to join in with. When you work with people that's sure to bring them together.'

'Yes, that might work...' I said.

'Brand promoters,' said Aruna.

'Sorry?'

'I read about this in a newspaper. Apparently beer and cigarette firms are now employing ordinary people to promote their goods. What they do is sit in bars and just talk to their friends about how good Marlborough cigarettes are, or they order Budweisers very loudly, so that the whole bar can hear. The idea is that people don't listen to adverts any more, but they will be affected by ordinary people around them. So what we do is employ a load of Christian young people to go in and talk in a very loud voice about how good church is.'

'Julian already does that,' I pointed out. 'Or at least he does the "talk in a very loud voice" bit.'

They began to warm to their task now. One person suggested a special user-friendly worship service on a Saturday night, another talked of friendship programmes where one person was given responsibility for befriending another.

In the end, I noticed how Andy was sitting quietly.

'Andy?' I said. 'What do you think?'

He smiled. 'All this talk of doing things for them. All this talk of programmes and projects. Why don't you just talk to them? Why don't you listen to them? Why don't you ask them to do something for us?'

There was silence round the table.

'Or,' said someone, 'we could put up a set of promotional posters around the walls...'

And they were off again.

Cheers
Chris

From: Chris Francis@Tabernacle.ch.uk
To: Patricia Ryan, P.Ryan@bigplace.com
Subject: Re: Closing the open door

Hi Pat,

The whole discussion about integrating the two sides of the youthwork got me thinking. So what I've decided to do is force the issue. We're all going on a youth weekend.

First, I had to get the money sorted and, as usual, that meant taking a budget proposal to last night's leader's meeting. Here's how it went.

Me: I want to organise a youth weekend away.

Pastor: Good idea.

Dennis (the treasurer): Excellent.

Cecily: Ah, yes, how well I remember the house parties I had when I was young. So many weekends spent in the Shalom Centre for Strict Evangelical Fellowship in Frinton. I remember one year, 1956 I think it was... (This went on for 17 minutes.)

Pastor: Yes, well, thank you Cecily. I think the meeting thoroughly approves, Chris.

Me: I want to make the weekend a mix of Christians and non-Christians.

Pastor: Super.

Me: And get in a good speaker...

Dennis: Of course.

Me: With loads of activities and everything.

Cecily: Wonderful!

Me: So all we need to do is agree a budget for the church to underwrite.

There is a stony silence. The mood darkens.

Dennis: Surely you can't be suggesting the church subsidises it? It must be self-funding, with all participants paying for their accommodation.

Me: Well, some of them will, but I want to be sure to be able to offer it to kids who don't have much money.

Pastor: (Rallying to offer support, but noticing that Dennis already has his calculator out) I'm sure we'd all want to support this kind of thing.

Cecily: Oh yes. And if money is really a problem, I could probably get you a discount at the Shalom Centre for Strict Evangelical Fellowship. Of course, it's more of a retirement home these days, but if you could promise not to make much noise...

Dennis: I know that youthwork needs resources, of course it does. Why, only last month I authorised two new table tennis balls. But a venture this size needs funding.

Me: Exactly. That's why I've drawn up this list of what the church should put up. Those who can pay will pay. Those who can't will be specially invited.

Dennis: But we haven't got the funds.

Me: Then we have to find them!

And so it went on. In the end the meeting resolved to:

1) Look into the matter further.

2) Appoint a steering group to set up a programme.

3) Write to Mrs Evangeline Simcox of the Shalom Centre for Strict Evangelical Fellowship to inquire about availability.

I can cope with loving my enemies. It's my friends who cause the problems.

Cheers
Chris

From: Julian@redemption.judgement.co.uk
To: Patricia Ryan, P.Ryan@bigplace.com
Subject: Youth leader madness

Dear Mrs Ryan (I am assuming you have entered the holy sacrament of matrimony. Please excuse me if you are still a handmaiden in waiting – Jer. 29:6.)

I am writing to you with concerns over our youth leader, Chris. He has given me to understand that you are involved in what he calls 'mentoring'. (I assume, as you are of the female persuasion that this does not involve any AUTHORITY over him, not any actual SPEAKING IN CHURCH, but that is another matter.1 Tim. 2:12; 1 Cor. 11:10.)

Not to put too fine a point on it, we think he may be MAD. It is possible that he may be under the sway of some HERETICAL cult, but I think it more likely to be simple madness.

It all came to a head last week, when we were having a planning meeting. Chis is very keen on what he calls 'youth involvement', although I have always felt that this shows a LAMENTABLE LACK OF LEADERSHIP. (Acts 1:20; 2 Sam. 7:10,11; Neh. 12:31)

The item under discussion was a plan he has for a youth weekend away (Gen. 18:23). We discussed many possibilities but I first began to realise that something was WRONG when we suggested names. Vanessa's suggestion that it be called 'The Enormous Love-In' was rightly rejected for its overtones of CARNALITY (Rom. 6:19). Glenda – who has always struck me as being overly concerned with the WORLD and less concerned with our HEAVENLY future (2 Pet. 3:13) suggested we call it 'The Putting out Deckchairs on the Titanic while Living on the Fault-line and Waiting for the Eve of Destruction Weekend'. Unfortunately, such a long sentence brought on an attack of her asthma and she had to have a lie down. I offered to PRAY for HEALING but was ignored. (Jas. 5:14; Lk. 4:40; Ex. 29:10)

Anyway, after Andy had given his usual inane suggestions (Prov. 10:8) I ventured that which had been given unto me, namely that we should call it 'BE RESTORED AND SAVED TO REDEMPTION AND PARADISE'. Chris rejected this on the grounds that (a) it was off-putting for non-Christians and (b) the initials spelled bra strap. Naturally I was SHOCKED (Job 14:4; Tit. 1:15).

I ask you, is it NORMAL for a leader to OBJECT to statements of Christian DOCTRINE to the public (Ps. 40:10)? And is it HONOURABLE to mention items of FEMALE UNDERGARMENTS in an assembly of the SAINTS (Lev. 13:59)? And is it not a sign of MADNESS to then roll around on the floor LAUGHING for five minutes (Ecc. 7:6; Jas. 4:9)?

Anyway, after a while, order was restored. He APOLOGISED for laughing so much and went to change his TROUSERS.

Needless to say I was not disposed to offer further suggestions, even though I had a SUREFIRE IDEA for the weekend – namely to make it a Luis Palau Fan Club convention. Instead, I held my peace, while the others discussed more WORLDLY items for inclusion such as games, events and what they called 'late-night entertainment' (Ps. 127:2; Is. 5:11).

This is not the first time that my reverend and dare I say it, inspired, suggestions have been laughed at. I try to give him tracts and improving reading but I suspect he never opens them. Even the GOLDEN WORDS of the Reverend Murdo McBrightly fail to move him (Prov. 16:24; Num. 12:6)

For this reason I suspect there may be more to this than simple worldliness or even his undoubted TRIVIALITY. I implore you to urge Chris to seek COUNSELLING, sage ADVICE or even ELECTRO-SHOCK THERAPY. Is it right for a youth group leader to openly laugh at the ZEAL and EARNESTNESS of those he is supposed to be discipling (Is. 29:20; Hos. 7:5; Ps. 1:1; 1 Thes. 5:11)? Or is this rather a sign of sickness, degradation and ungodly footwear (Ex. 12:11; Mk. 6:9)?

I look forward to your PRAYERFUL response.

Yours through him, by them, with that and over there,

Julian

From: Chris Francis@Tabernacle.ch.uk
To: Patricia Ryan, P.Ryan@bigplace.com
Subject: Integration (2)

Hi Pat,

Thanks a lot. It's good to have support and advice from others. However, with regard to the youth weekend, there remains the issue of integration and I don't know how many of the non-church kids will want to come.

Yesterday I had another delegation from the youth group. (Well, actually they called themselves a 'delectation' but I think that was just a Freudian slip from Vanessa.) They were concerned about the make-up of the weekend.

'We wanted to see you,' explained Vanessa. 'Because we think it ought to be more of a "bonding" exercise for the kids in the church.'

The image of me and Vanessa involved in a bonding session was not one I wanted to dwell on, so I asked them what they meant.

'We have different needs,' replied Aruna. 'We need some discipling and nurturing, a chance to grow as a group.'

'Yes I understand that,' I said. 'But this is a great chance to introduce a whole lot of new people to Jesus. Isn't that what we're supposed to be doing? Isn't that what Tuesday nights are all about?'

To be honest this probably wasn't likely to sway them. The fact is that I've noticed more and more on Tuesday nights that there is a real gap between the church kids and the kids who come in from the 'outside'.

'Look,' I said. 'When we meet on Sunday nights, that's a real chance for you to get some spiritual input. But this weekend will be such a great opportunity.'

'But we were hoping that this would be something just for us,' said Vanessa.

At that moment I received support from an unlikely source. Julian (who'd only dropped by to deliver the latest tract from the Rev Murdo McBrightly – a small pamphlet entitled 'Purifying Pain – How to get Spiritual Nourishment out of Minor Diseases') joined the argument.

'If what we believe is true,' he said, 'then how can we not take every opportunity to share it?'

'Exactly,' I added.

'Even if those we talk to are infidels and unbelievers...'

'Yes, thank you Julian.'

'Who tend to throw mud at you and call you "Gimp head".'

'Right, good point...'

'But what care I if they rend my bones and throw me to the wild beasts?' he cried with sudden passion. 'Let them cast me before the lions and the elephants and the zebras! What do I care for the blows and buffets of the godless mob? If I must die then let me die for the cause!'

There was a pause.

'Er, we're only talking about a weekend away,' I said.

'Well, we've made our point,' said Aruna.

'I'll bear it in mind.'

At that point the meeting broke up, which was just as well, as I could see Julian gearing up for another onslaught. He always gets like this after reading John Bunyan.

So what do I do?

Cheers
Chris

From: Chris Francis@Tabernacle.ch.uk
To: Patricia Ryan, P.Ryan@bigplace.com
Subject: Sven

Pat,

There are times when youthwork is the best job in the world; when you feel that what you are doing is significant, important, when it even feels thrilling.

And then there are times like these.

I don't know if you remember Sven, the ex-druid and underground eco-warrior. For a while he was going out with Glenda, but the relationship foundered ('I hardly ever see him,' she told me. 'And when I do he's covered with mud.'). This was probably for the best. Glenda's a great girl but her heart rules her head a lot of the time. I think there was a point when she'd have chucked everything in and run away to join him in his subterranean paradise, but we're over that now.

Anyway, I'd kept in contact with Sven and met him every Wednesday for coffee at 'The Spinach Shack', the local organic wholefood restaurant. (Well, it was coffee for me, Sven always had a mug of chamomile and seaweed tea.)

Gradually our talks got us deeper and deeper. I mean, the lad is really seeking, really looking for meaning. We ranged over everything – the meaning of life, the problem of suffering, the corruption of modern society, the need for belonging, you name it, we did it.

'Sometimes I just feel so alone,' he said to me a few days ago. 'Sometimes I feel that I'm the only one who thinks this way.'

'What about your family?' I asked.

'Oh, they don't speak to me any more, man,' he replied. 'They hate what I do. It's like, everything I stand for is against them.'

'What does your dad do?' I asked.

'He's a builder.'

'Oh. What does he build?'

'Roads.'

There was a pause. 'Yes,' I said at last. 'I can see how your career of chaining yourself to bulldozers might bring you into conflict with him.'

He stabbed his herbal teabag with a plastic stirrer. 'I try to explain, but they think it's just a phase I'm going through.'

He looked at me.

'Whenever the older generation don't want to listen to you, they call it a phase,' he said. 'They think that one day, you'll grow up and all these stupid ideas will disappear. Like acne.'

'Maybe they will,' I replied. 'The world is full of disillusioned activists.'

'Yeah, but you can't stop believing the truth, can you!' he demanded. 'If I stop believing what is right, if I stop fighting, then I... I'd rather be dead.'

'Not everyone loses it,' I said. 'Some keep on fighting. The problem is that a lot of people find out that what they were fighting for wasn't the real truth after all. Or, at least, not the whole truth.'

Then he said, 'Tell me the truth, then. Tell me what it's all about.'

So I told him. I told him about sin and forgiveness; about love and Jesus and salvation. The words poured out, like water from a bottle. And he drank every drop. I could see it all go home and I know he understood.

When I'd finished, there was a pause.

'I need to think about this,' he said.

'Sure,' I replied. 'Take what time you need.'

We arranged to meet the next day at the same place. That night I prayed really hard. And I know this shouldn't make any difference whatsoever, but I really like Sven. He's sharp, he's funny, he really cares about things. Which is why it was a hammer blow when he didn't turn up. I sat for an hour, but no show. I left messages for him, but he's never been the easiest guy to contact.

Then, this afternoon I met him in the street.

'Hi,' I said, trying to appear nonchalant. 'I thought we were supposed to meet. What happened?'

He looked at me and it was like there was a shadow between us.

'I changed my mind,' he said.

And that was it. He walked on.

I get sick of these books that make out evangelism is so easy; that all we have to do is have courage and speak the truth. Well, I had courage, I told a friend the truth and he refused it.

And before you hit the 'reply' button, I know all the right answers. I know that relational youthwork is hard. I understand that we have to get used to rejection and 'we must have faith'. Tomorrow I will see things a bit clearer. Tomorrow, maybe, I'll get things back into perspective.

But today I'm tired and I'm sad.

Cheers
Chris

From: Chris Francis@Tabernacle.ch.uk
To: Patricia Ryan, P.Ryan@bigplace.com
Subject: Two herds

Pat,

The tension bubbling under about the proposed youth weekend has refused to go away. The church kids still feel like their 'club' is being infiltrated. The unchurched kids are keen, but I think they feel the tension as well. It's a peculiar thing – it's not that the two groups dislike each other – indeed some of them are good friends. It's more that there's a kind of battle for ownership going on. I feel like David Attenborough watching two rival herds marking out their territory.

Anyway, in the end I decided that before the youth weekend I would take some of the church kids away to a big Christian event. If they want a time of bonding and nurturing, fine. So I got hold of some brochures and everybody made a choice. Vanessa wanted to go to 'Love Europe', but I think she thought that was an activity week. Julian wanted to go to the 53rd Ambleside Strict Bible Exegesis Convention, where Rev Murdo McBrightly was speaking. I vetoed this on the grounds that their entire youth programme consisted of some choruses from the *Golden Bells* chorus book (1923) and someone called 'Uncle Brian and his Puppet Parables'.

In the end we chose the big one: a week's camping in the countryside at 'Autumn Belt – the festival for the Souled Out Generation'.

I made it clear to whoever wanted to go that I would provide transport and nothing else. This was not a 'church' trip, I was not going in an official capacity and anyway, I wanted to go to all the seminars, celebrations and concerts myself.

The journey down was uneventful apart from Julian objecting to our group rendition of 'Ten Green Bottles' on the grounds that it encouraged drinking. And we travelled during a September mini heat-wave making it stiflingly hot in the minibus. (Of course, the moment we turned in through the gates of the park where the event was being held, the heavens opened. It poured for the rest of the week, but I comforted myself with the thought that at least in the rain the toilets don't smell.)

On the whole it worked well. There were enough different things to keep people going, good times of varied worship and some thought-provoking seminars. Truth to tell I hardly saw them from morning to evening. Vanessa seemed to spend most of her time in the coffee tent, being 'counselled' by a hunky-looking youthworker. I thought about telling him that she actually was a Christian, but she looked so happy I hadn't the heart. Glenda spent much of her time debating the nature of art with a nun called Sister Griselda. Aruna went to a series of debates on 'The Epistemological Nature of the Divine Imperative'. I asked her what she thought of them, and she said they were OK, but a bit superficial.

What really struck them, however, was the worship.

'Wasn't the music fantastic!' exclaimed Giles in the minibus on the way back.

'And the atmosphere,' enthused Vanessa.

'I thought some of the preachers were hermeneutically unsound,' said Julian. 'But I approved of their missionary zeal.'

'The problem is,' said Andy, 'now we've got to go home.'

'What do you mean?' I asked.

'Well, we've spent a week with really fantastic worship and all that, and now we've got to go back to Briglimpton-flippin'-Tabernacle.'

There was a murmur of agreement.

'Their idea of radical worship is when the organist wears a bow tie,' said Glenda.

'Well maybe we can introduce some of the songs at the next youth service,' I suggested.

'It won't be the same,' said Giles. 'It never is.'

'Look,' I said. 'You've had a great time. But nobody can live on the mountain-top forever.'

Andy looked at me. 'Why not?' he asked.

'Er... they just can't,' I said. 'They get altitude sickness. Or it snows. Or they fall off or something.' I tried a different tack, aware that my arguments weren't entirely convincing. 'Look at it like this – it's nice to have a box of chocolates sometimes, but if you eat nothing but chocolates then you throw up.'

There was a pause while everyone considered this charming analogy.

'I still wish church could be more like that was,' said Andy.

'Yeah,' agreed Glenda. 'It was so alive.'

In truth, they all knew that I didn't have an answer. No one in their right mind wants every day to be like Autumn Belt. But I know they want more chocolates in their life and less spiritual roughage.

They enjoyed their week. They were noticeably more on fire afterwards, and they were really challenged by some of the speakers. Now the problem: do I bring them down off the mountain top, or do I have to drag the church higher up the slope?

Cheers
Chris

From: Chris Francis@Tabernacle.ch.uk
To: Patricia Ryan, P.Ryan@bigplace.com
Subject: Sandra's first visit to church

Hi Pat,

There's this girl called Sandra. She comes from an almost completely unchurched background but she's been coming to Tuesday night group and we've had some great discussions. (She's a friend of Vanessa's, but happily, doesn't share Vanessa's desire to engage me in 'one-to-one team-building'.)

Anyway, imagine my surprise last Sunday night when there she was. Sitting in church. Admittedly she was right at the back, but those of us who are regular listeners to the pastor's series on 'Trees of the Old Testament' have long since discovered that this is the best place to be.

So I played it cool. Said hello and sat a few seats away.

From the start she looked bemused. She began talking loudly to Vanessa who, much to my surprise, chatted back at the same volume. Then they burst into giggles during the prayers. Julian was leading worship – he had on his special rainbow striped cagoule for the occasion – and we just finished one of his favourite worship songs: 'At the Sight of our Sandals, the Enemies Flee'.

Sandra turned to Vanessa and said, in a remarkably loud voice, 'That was rubbish, wasn't it? It didn't make no sense at all.'

Julian, unfortunately, was unable to resist the challenge.

'I'm sure we all appreciated that deeply moving and symbolic song,' he said, to no one in particular. 'Perhaps this would be a good time to have some QUIET prayer.'

'It didn't even rhyme...' complained a voice.

'Some SILENT prayer,' repeated Julian.

'And anyway, I don't even wear sandals.'

'DO YOU MIND? WE'RE TRYING TO HAVE SOME SILENT, CONTEMPLATIVE PRAYER HERE!' yelled Julian. 'JUST PUT A SOCK IN IT WILL YOU?' His voice trailed off as he realised that he was yelling. 'Er... I meant all that in love,' he added.

After that the service continued along normal lines. Apart from the point where Sandra put some money in the collection and then asked for change. Oh, and the bit during the sermon where she called out to me: 'Have you got any idea what he's on about?' (For a moment I was placed in a difficult position. The fact was that I hadn't a clue what the pastor was on about, but I didn't want to admit it in front of everyone. Luckily he was so absorbed in his exposition of the spiritual significance of gopher wood he just carried straight on.)

So all, in all, it was a huge relief when the service ended. I headed straight for Sandra, all prepared to give her a diplomatic little chat on church etiquette. But I was too late. There, bearing down on her was Mrs Golightly.

Never has a name been less appropriate. Mrs Golightly is roughly the size of a small asteroid. Whenever she approaches you it is like being engulfed by a solar eclipse. The sky turns dark, the air turns cold. And if she doesn't approve of something you've done... Well, I've seen her reduce grown deacons to quivering masses of jelly. Personally I've never had any trouble with her, but only because I give in at the earliest opportunity.

'You girl,' she boomed at Sandra. 'What's your name?'

'Sandra,' she said.

Mrs Golightly drew herself up to her full width.

'Would you like a cup of tea?' she said.

There was a kind of hushed silence in the church as everyone's brains tried to cope with the fact that Sandra was still standing.

'Ooh yeah,' said Sandra. 'That'd be good. Mind you, I'm dying for a fag.'

She reached into her bag and pulled out a packet of Rothmans. The congregation tensed. This was it. This was where Mrs Golightly picked the girl up and threw her through the stained glass windows. But she just smiled.

'Not in here, dear,' she said. Her voice lowered to a whisper. 'Some people are a bit sniffy about that kind of thing.'

'Oh right,' said Sandra.

And they went off to get a cup of tea.

After Sandra had gone home, I went over to Mrs Golightly.

'Thank you,' I said.

'For what?'

'For not having a go at her. For accepting her.'

'Oh that,' said Mrs Golightly. She sipped her tea. 'Years ago,' she said, 'I persuaded my husband to come to church with me. He belched during the Bible reading.' She turned to me and there was an unexpected sadness in her eyes. 'He got such looks from everyone around him that he never ever came back. I always vowed that that would never happen again.'

'Thanks.'

'And anyway, she was right,' she added, pointing to Julian. 'None of his songs make any sense whatsoever.'

Cheers
Chris

From: Chris Francis@Tabernacle.ch.uk
To: Patricia Ryan, P.Ryan@bigplace.com
Subject: The weekend starts here!

Hi Pat,

It's Friday. It's 8 p.m. and we have finally arrived at the long-awaited youth weekend. I've brought the laptop with me so I can give you regular reports.

The journey here was a little fraught. We booked a 24-seater coach, piled everything on to it and set out. We hadn't gone 50 yards when Julian declared that the bus was inhabited by 'a spirit of gambling'. Apparently he'd found a used scratch-card down the back of one of the seats.

'We should stop and have a cleansing service,' he said.

'The only cleansing this bus needs is a good wash,' I replied. 'We're late. We'll go on.'

'You always ignore my prophecies!' said Julian. 'Well, don't blame me if we break down.'

After another three miles Vanessa suddenly revealed that she was car-sick and that she needed to sit up the front.

Unsurprisingly this meant squeezing in next to me. She spent most of the journey trying to look pale and sick in the hope that I would notice her. A couple of times she asked if I would wipe her fevered brow. I pretended to be asleep.

We were roughly halfway when the bus started to shudder like a congregation that has been asked to tithe. Then it died altogether and we coasted to a stop on the hard shoulder.

There was a coughing from the direction of Julian's seat. I refused to look round, but I could hear him praying under his breath.

In the end Andy fixed the problem in about five minutes. He did explain it to me but I am mechanically illiterate, so it made no sense. All that mattered was that we were moving again.

We arrived here about two hours ago. We have booked into something called 'Camp Craggy' which consists of five log cabins nailed to the side of a mountain in the Peak District. I think it used to be a Youth Detention Centre until it was taken over by Christians who immediately pronounced it too luxurious and removed the heating. The staff all appear to be ex-American footballers called Clint or Bud or Larry and the main course for the evening meal was, if my taste-buds are accurate, spaghetti cooked in polyfilla.

Still, the kids seem to enjoy it, especially the opening 'paintball' game. Even Julian had a go, although he refused to remove his cagoule. As it is bright orange with 'John 3:16' written on the back in black letters it made him a bit of a sitting target. A couple of the kids have been talking about the abseiling tower – they are really scared! We especially asked for this as a trust exercise. It will do them the world of good.

Cheers
Chris

From: Chris Francis@Tabernacle.ch.uk
To: Patricia Ryan, P.Ryan@bigplace.com
Subject: Why am I awake?

Hi Pat,

It's Saturday morning, about 7 a.m. I have been awake for three hours now.

They finally went to sleep around midnight. The girls are sleeping in 'Shackleton Lodge' with Julie and Sandra, who is helping out on the weekend. The boys are with me and Andy in the cellblock that is known as 'Scott Cabin'. (All the rooms and lodges are named after Antarctic explorers. They would have felt at home.)

After a few hours sleep, we were woken by the sound of guitar-playing from Julian's room. He then burst out of the door and proceeded to walk around the hut playing Graham Kendrick songs and shouting out Bible verses. I yelled at him to get back into bed, but he didn't seem to hear. After a while we realised he was still asleep: it was the first recorded instance of someone sleep prayer-marching.

After that we were all awake, so we went out for a walk. The kids are still nervous about the abseiling. I wound them up with stories of ropes breaking and safety clips coming undone. It makes a change to see them in a different setting. At home they are all so confident and sure of themselves.

Cheers,

**Chris of the Antarctic
Scott Cabin, The Frozen North**

From: Vanessa Bodie <Vanessa@fluffy.pink.com>
To: Patricia Ryan <P.Ryan@bigplace.com>
Subject: Rejection and hurt

Hello

Excuse me writing like this but I've sneaked a quick go on Chris' computer and I'm sure he wouldn't mind me asking you a question as I know you are a sister who understands women and especially hormones and innermost feelings and all that. Could you have a word with Chris? Only we went out for a walk this afternoon and I fell and twisted my ankle really, really badly and he didn't even stop to carry me back even though I asked him a lot. He just carried on walking and told me that if I was really hurt I didn't have to do the abseiling.

I don't think that is very Christian, do you? I thought at least he should have done that laying on of hands bit, especially as I'd brought along a bottle of oil for when I got injured. In the end some of the other boys carried me back on a bit of plank and I snagged my tights.

Lots of luv,

Vanessa

From: Chris Francis@Tabernacle.ch.uk
To: Patricia Ryan, P.Ryan@bigplace.com
Subject: Signs of hope

Hi Pat,

Well, tonight was the big evangelistic talk. The guy speaking was either Clint or Bud. Or it could have been Larry. Good speaker though. Great story. The guy had it all, money, success and gave it all up to establish these Christian camps for kids.

(Personally I think he shouldn't have given up all the money. He should have used it to buy better insulation on the cabins. There was ice inside my duvet tonight.)

Anyway, the kids seemed to listen, but no one made any signs of commitment. I felt a bit depressed and was lying on my bunk after it was all over, when there was a knock at the door. At first I thought it was Julian come to complain about his cagoule again (I told him that trying to get the paint off it with paint stripper was not a good idea) but it was actually a guy called Jake from one of the schools I visit.

He'd listened to Clint or Bud (or Larry) and wanted to ask some questions. He'd even read a bit in the Bible which he'd found by the side of the bed, which talked about 'gaining the whole world and losing your soul' and he wanted to know what that meant.

We had a great talk. He didn't become a Christian – and I didn't ask him. But the seeds are there. He's started to think about it. And that's the kind of thing that makes this job worthwhile.

Tomorrow is the big abseil. I can't wait to see the look on their faces.

Cheers

Chris

From: Julian@redemption.judgement.co.uk
To: Patricia Ryan, P.Ryan@bigplace.com
Subject: Youth leader in peril!

Greetings Sister in the Lord,

This is an URGENT request for prayer (Rom. 12:12; Col. 4:2). Chris is stuck halfway down the abseiling tower, and refusing to move. Everyone else got down OK, but he appears to have had something of a BREAKDOWN. He is just hanging there, with his eyes shut (Rom. 11:8).

I have exhorted him to TRUST in the LORD (Jn. 14:1), but he answered that he would never trust anybody ever again. So it appears to be a CRISIS of FAITH as well. Please pray for us. The EMERGENCY services have been called, but they are having difficulty prising his FINGERS from the frame of the TOWER (Mk. 7:33).

Yours in him, by them, with that and shake before use,

Julian

PS: We need him down because he has the KEYS to the MINIBUS (Mt. 16:19; Rev. 1:18).

St Thomas's

From: Chris Francis@Tabernacle.ch.uk

To: Patricia Ryan, P.Ryan@bigplace.com

Subject: Apocalypse now

Hi Pat,

Thanks for the card. I've almost recovered from the events of the away weekend. The doctors say it's nothing to worry about – apparently Post-Traumatic Stress Disorder is not uncommon among youthworkers. I'm all right as long as I don't have to go up any heights. I stood on the chair to change a light bulb yesterday and it took me 15 minutes to get down.

By the way, we're holding a party and Andy's decided on a 'post-apocalyptic' theme.

'I want it to look like a bomb has dropped,' he said, 'it's a party in a bunker.'

He's done a great job. Camouflage netting and blackout material on the walls… and loads of tins and supplies: ham, tuna, beans and spaghetti, and packets of sugar, flour and instant mashed potato.

'Wow! Where did you get all this?' I asked.

Suddenly, there came a howl of rage. Within seconds, Hurricane Stanley blew in.

'What are you doing?' He pointed at the tins. 'That's mine.'

'We're only borrowing it,' said Andy. 'We found it in a cupboard.'

'That's my survival cupboard!' said Stanley.

'I'm sorry?' I said.

'Global warming and all that… I've seen a film about it… We have to take precautions, get in supplies!'

'I think the best thing,' I said, 'would be if you came to our party. Then you could be close to the supplies if there's a sudden disaster.'

'I don't want to go to any parties – '

'Oh go on,' I said. 'Otherwise I might have to start asking questions about where all this stuff came from. I mean, I can't help noticing that you've got a loaf shaped like a sheaf of wheat there. My memory isn't good, but I'd say it looks exactly like our harvest display from September.'

Stanley looked at me.

'How much are the tickets?' he asked.

Cheers
Chris

PS: I've been asked to go and speak at St Thomas's next week – the big church on the edge of town. What I'd give for their resources!

From: Chris Francis@Tabernacle.ch.uk
To: Patricia Ryan, P.Ryan@bigplace.com
Subject: The blues

Hi Pat,

There ought to be a module in youthwork training on 'Persuading church treasurers to part with cash, possibly using force'.

You see, I have this vision. It's not a huge vision as visions go. I'm not trying to achieve world peace and mend the ozone layer. I don't want to free the people of East Briglimpton and lead them into the Promised Land. I just want a dedicated youth centre. Somewhere where we can set things up and leave them. Somewhere we don't have to share with the ladies' fellowship and the toddler groups and the weight watchers and the pastor's Thursday night adult Bible study class on 'Skin Diseases of the Scriptures'.

The pastor handed over to me to outline what I saw as major items for expense next year. So I went for it.

'What I really want,' I said, 'is a dedicated youth centre.' There was a silence round the table. Everyone looked at me as though I had suddenly started speaking Swahili. Eventually Dennis, the treasurer, spoke.

'Hmph,' he said.

'Somewhere the kids could have as their own,' I continued. 'Somewhere dedicated to them.'

'Hmph,' said the treasurer.

'I was thinking about that old building out the back. You know, where all that rubbish is.'

'Hmph.'

I looked at him.

'Would you stop going "hmph" for a bit?' I asked. 'It's not very encouraging.'

There was a pause. He was obviously trying to work out what 'encouraging' meant. In the end he gave up and just said, 'Hmph.'

'Look, if you're not going to support the idea, fine,' I said. 'I'll find the money myself. But I thought at least we could look at whether or not the church had any funds put aside for developing those rooms.'

There was a general rustling of papers and the treasurer started to go 'hmph' again, but by this time I was beginning to look slightly threatening, so he stopped midway through his 'hmph' and turned it into a cough.

'We can't afford it,' he said. 'Never mind a dedicated youth centre, it's as much as we can do to pay a dedicated youthworker.'

'Well can't we set up some kind of appeal or something?'

'It would clash,' said the pastor.

'What with?'

'All the other appeals we've got going this year. We've got to replace the organ, you know.'

By this time I was seriously beginning to lose it.

'Replace the organ?' I ranted. 'Replace the organ? We're talking about people here. This is a chance to invest in the future and you're talking about spending thousands of pounds on an instrument that sounds like someone castrating an elephant.'

'It was a diaconate decision,' said someone else. 'You were at the meeting.'

They always get me on this one. Of course I was at the meeting. But I wasn't listening, was I? I'm the youthworker, for heaven's sake. You can't expect me to listen during meetings.

'Anyway, it's not just the organ, is it?' The pastor consulted his notebook. 'We've got the roof appeal, the carpet appeal, new hymn-books, new seats, and the old boiler needs replacing.'

I stared at him.

'Look,' he said. 'I don't enjoy all this. I don't enjoy saying "no".' He paused. 'Well actually I do enjoy it, but that's not the point. It's a question of priorities. You'll just have to wait your turn.'

'When will it be my turn?'

'In about eight year's time.'

'What?' I exploded.

'There's no need to get angry,' said the pastor. 'I'm sure we can work something out. We're not saying that it can't happen – '

'Just that it won't.'

'Look, there are other people in the church beside the youth,' he said. 'You never seem to appreciate that fact.'

In the end I gave up. I just didn't have the energy to fight it. A normal budget was approved allowing me full authority to go and buy a new table tennis bat and some new board games. I resisted the urge to shout hallelujah and proclaim a holiday.

What made it all so much worse is that a couple of weeks ago I went and spoke at the youth event at St Thomas's. They have a youth centre, a huge team of committed volunteers, a full-time youthworker and a budget the size of my telephone number. What have I got? A few table tennis bats, a broken game of Twister, a team of nutters and a leadership with all the vision of a blindfolded mole. I know we're not a big church, but I'm fed up having to skimp along on a budget. What's the point?

Can anyone tell me why I bother?

Cheers
Chris

From: Chris Francis@Tabernacle.ch.uk
To: Patricia Ryan, P.Ryan@bigplace.com
Subject: Out of the blue...

Hi Pat,

On the face of it, last Tuesday's post was nothing out of the ordinary: a couple of bills, a letter from my mother telling me to eat more and get more exercise, an invitation to an event called 'The Global Evangelism Conference' to be held in a scout hut in Rhyl, and a small book entitled *Pre-Destination for Dummies* by the Rev Murdo McBrightly.

It was only as I was about to file the whole lot carefully in the bin that I noticed another letter at the bottom of the pile. Posh, cream-coloured envelope; first class stamp; addressed to 'Chris Francis – Personal.'

For a moment I thought it was another of Vanessa's requests for 'one-to-one mentoring' although those are usually written on pink Barbie notepaper in green ink. But it wasn't from Vanessa, it was from St Thomas's. You'll recall I went to speak there recently – the big church with the dedicated youth centre, a huge and committed team of volunteers... and their clergy get company cars. (The nearest I get is borrowing the pastor's moped.)

To my shock and astonishment, the vicar was writing to me to see if I might be interested in applying for the job of youthworker. They were 'impressed with my style' and wondered if I was thinking of 'moving on'.

Naturally I got in touch, went to meet them, and worked very hard at pretending that this kind of thing happens to me all the time. We talked for a while and then they offered me the job, there and then. There's no rush so I have some time to think it over.

Oh, who am I kidding? I mean, what is there to think over? I've been headhunted! They have everything I've dreamed of. At St Thomas's, youthwork is high-priority, here it ranks just above cleaning the toilets and just below the flower rota. They have a budget and real resources, I have a broken pool table. Most importantly, they have a team. I have more of a group therapy unit.

This is a chance to actually achieve something. All right, so I have achieved some things here, but I've done it in spite of the church and everything around me. I mean, never mind support and encouragement, I've seen more supportive goldfish. I haven't been doing youthwork here, I've been surviving it.

Of course I will miss the kids. They're a good lot, despite their eccentricities. There is real faith there, albeit growing in a confused, rambling, eccentric and occasionally even heretical manner. I'm fond of them. I'm even fond of Julian, in a perverse 'not-very-fond-of-him-at-all' sort of way. It will be difficult to leave them, and I've spent the last few nights trying to rationalise it. You see, I know they'll be disappointed and even hurt. But I guess one of the lessons you have to learn as a young person is that things change. People move on.

Of course, for some of them, that's the problem with their life all the time – everyone moves on. I had lunch with Julian the other day – it was the anniversary of his dad's death. I think he appreciated the thought, even if he did try to cast a demon out of me whilst saying grace.

But that's beside the point. The point is, when the time comes for them to leave, will they think about me? No, they'll pursue their own dreams and ambitions and calling… and that's all I'm doing. No one has ever taken me to lunch on the anniversary of Sarah's death. No one has ever been bothered to ask.

So I've phoned the vicar of St Thomas's and accepted his offer. I'll be moving there after Easter. Everything about this feels right. Really it does.

Anyway, I have to make plans. There is a lot to get organised.

I've made the right decision, I'm sure of it. I mean, it would be nice if things were a bit clearer, you know a hand appearing and writing on the wall 'mene mene go to St Thomas's' or something. But that doesn't happen. We have to make our own decisions and I feel very secure about this one. I'm sure it's right...

What do you think?

Cheers
Chris

From: Chris Francis@Tabernacle.ch.uk
To: Patricia Ryan, P.Ryan@bigplace.com
Subject: Responses

Hi Pat,

Thanks for the email. I appreciate your response. Of course, the issues have changed slightly now as I am moving to St Thomas's. I met with the pastor yesterday. To my astonishment he was very supportive and helpful and keen that 'you should do what's best for you'. But, coming away from the meeting, I'm not sure he's right. It's not just what's best for me, is it? It's what's best for the young people as well. And, I guess, what's best for the kingdom – but that's always a tricky one to work out.

Not that I am having second thoughts. I mean, if nothing else, this might persuade this place that they have to take youthwork seriously and make it a higher priority.

I'm still not sure of the right way to break it to the youth group. We had a sort of committee meeting here tonight – to look at what they want to do in the coming months. As usual, the limp hand of apathy ruled.

Anyway, I asked them for their responses on the past few months, too.

Andy: It was OK.

Vanessa: (Simpering) Whatever you think is best, Chris.

Julian: If you ask me – and speaking prophetically – I think our activities have smacked too much of the frivolous and not enough on the godly.

Me: Well, what does everyone suggest then?

Pause. Long silence.

Vanessa: (Brightly) Why don't you decide, Chris.

Andy: Yeah, that's a good idea.

Julian: I will be praying for you.

Chris: Great. Thanks very much.

And so it goes on...

Cheers
Chris

From: Chris Francis@Tabernacle.ch.uk

To: Patricia Ryan, P.Ryan@bigplace.com

Subject: Called or headhunted?

Pat,

OK. I take your point. I know they're not stupid. I know that if I move to a bigger church in the same town they'll realise that it has something to do with a 'bigger and better' opportunity. But what am I to do?

Of course it would be better to go to another town, but I haven't been offered the job in another town, have I? I've been offered it here. And it's because I'm good at what I do, which at least they recognise.

I don't go for all this 'calling' business, either. Never have. I mean, why do we insist on it? People don't feel 'called' to be plumbers, do they? They don't feel 'called' to be dustmen or dentists or even doctors. They just want to do it.

And this is something I want to do. I'm never sure whether I have been 'called' or whether I just love youthwork and want to do what I love. Do you think God sees a difference?

I sometimes think that Christians spiritualise everything too much. We turn jobs into 'ministries' to make them, and us, seem more important. I mean, I think what I do is important – I don't need to call it something special. The difference between a job and a vocation is that you get paid less for pursuing a vocation. Either everything is a ministry or nothing is.

But call it a ministry and then people expect miracles out of you. They expect you to work all the hours for hardly anything and then feed 5,000 people with only some sliced bread and a tin of pilchards. You're supposed to be here to help young people with their problems, but then when a problem appears, you're the one who gets it in the neck.

Anyway, last night I told the youth group that I was leaving. It wasn't what you might call a 'relaxing' event.

We had our usual after-church Sunday night meeting. Julian was hosting a thought-provoking session on 'Sandals – The Lord's Choice of Footwear' and the meeting had degenerated into chaos after he insisted on casting out what he called 'a spirit of Doc Martens' from the room. Anyway, after everyone had thanked him for his words/called him an idiot/stopped laughing hysterically I asked them for their attention.

They knew something was up. Kids are like that – they can smell uncertainty at 30 yards. Also, they noticed that there was an extra packet of chocolate Hobnobs out – always a sign that I have something to say they won't like.

'This isn't easy for me to say,' I began. 'But I have something to tell you.'

'At last!' cried Julian. 'You are going to repent of your liberalism!'

'No,' I replied. 'It's not that.'

'What have we done wrong now, then?' asked Giles. 'Too noisy during the youth service? Have we messed up the hall again, by walking on the carpet in an aggressive manner? Or have we just been breathing too frequently?'

'You're getting paranoid,' I said. 'No, it's something more personal...'

Vanessa gave a little squeal of excitement.

'Is it how you've found true love in the person of someone much younger than you, whom you have ignored, but whose devotion has finally won your heart despite the fact that she is only four-foot eleven inches tall and wears braces?'

'Er... no.'

'Oh,' she said, crestfallen. 'Shame!'

'No,' I continued. 'You see, the thing is, that is, well, you see... er...'

I ground to a halt. There was a silence.

'He's leaving,' said a voice. It was Glenda.

'What?' asked Andy.

'He's leaving. He's going to join the capitalist running dogs of St Thomas's. Just because they've got more money and live in nicer houses.'

'It's not like that at all,' I protested.

'Of course it is. I was speaking to my cousin who goes there. She said they made you an offer you couldn't refuse.'

'You make them sound like the Mafia.'

She just shrugged.

'Leaving?' asked Julian. 'But you can't... I haven't saved you yet.'

'Look, I just felt it was time to move on,' I said, and went on to explain that it was nothing personal, I would still be around for a while, I would be sure to keep in touch, etc., etc.

I looked round at the faces. Some were upset. Some were apathetic. Some seemed quite pleased. And one face was exercising enormous self-control.

'I think Chris has been very good to tell us face-to-face,' said Vanessa. 'He has been very good to us all, and I think we owe it to him not to question his decision or make things difficult for him.'

'Thank you,' I said. 'I appreciate that.'

'And above all we must remain calm and not get all silly and hysterical about it,' she continued, with a rather worrying catch in her voice. 'Just because some of us had hopes...' she was now starting to twitch slightly and her lower lip was quivering. 'Hopes that we meant more to him than a bunch of kids who could be cast aside at any moment...'

'Yes, well, I think we should leave the subject now,' I said. But there was no stopping her.

'YOU BRUTE!' she wailed. 'YOU HEARTLESS MONSTER! YOU TOYED WITH OUR AFFECTIONS AND NOW YOU'VE JUST CAST US ASIDE LIKE... LIKE... LIKE A GREAT BIG CAST ASIDE THING! HOW COULD YOU DO IT? HOW?'

And she ran out of the room, sobbing hysterically. There was a pause.

'I think she's a bit upset,' said Julian.

'Look, I'm sorry to be going, really I am,' I said. 'But nothing lasts forever. Sooner or later you will all move on to different careers or to colleges and universities.'

'That's right,' said Glenda. 'But we're here now. And there will be more after us. And who's going to look after them?'

'There will be a new youthworker.'

'Oh yeah. I expect people will be queuing up to work here. The youthwork equivalent of Siberia. I don't blame you, Chris. We didn't really expect you to stay this long. I'd better go and comfort the Barbie girl,' said Glenda, and walked out.

Gradually the meeting dispersed. No one said anything more about it. They all drifted off.

I was so angry. They'd been totally, utterly, completely unfair. They'd made me feel guilty for something which I had every right to do. The only time I've put myself first since I've been here. Typical!

And yet I still feel a nagging worry – what if Glenda was right? Has everyone else left them? Am I really going where I feel called? Or am I just deserting a sinking ship?

I sat there for ages in the dark, just thinking about things.

They didn't even touch the chocolate Hobnobs.

Cheers
Chris

From: Chris Francis@Tabernacle.ch.uk
To: Patricia Ryan, P.Ryan@bigplace.com
Subject: The big announcement

Pat,

So I was all set. I had even started packing. Gathering together all those dog-eared copies of *Youthwork* from where they have been carefully filed (i.e. stuffed down the side of the sofa, under the bathroom mat, in the boiler cupboard, etc.) My guitar was in its flight case (not that I ever get to fly anywhere with it, but it looks good). Everything was in boxes. My books were boxed up. My clothes carefully folded before being stuffed into black bin liners. Only a few days to go.

And then the doorbell rang.

I opened the door to see a tall, slightly grubby individual with a face full of so many studs he looked like he had been caught in an explosion in an ear-ring factory.

'Hello Sven,' I said.

Yes, it was the ex-druid and underground eco-warrior. He was one of my biggest failures – or at least that's what it felt like. I haven't seen him for a while – partly because he's kept out of my way and partly because he frequents the local organic wholefood restaurant, while I gravitate towards the chippy.

'Hi there,' he said. 'You got time for a talk?'

'Sure,' I said.

He slouched in, slumped down on the sofa and gazed around the room, while I poured him a coffee and opened the chocolate Hobnobs.

'You going somewhere?'

I told him all about my move to St Thomas's, the new job, everything. He was strangely unimpressed.

'Can't say I blame you,' he said, helping himself to his fifth Hobnob. 'Getting out of this dump.'

'It's not a question of that,' I said. 'It's just a career move. I'm going to a new job.'

'Oh yeah?' he said. 'You're not running away from this one, then?'

By now I was getting a bit annoyed. Ever since I'd taken this job I'd had to listen to lectures and comments from people about my motives.

'Look,' I said, 'I'm going to another job. It's my decision and my life. I don't see what it's got to do with you, anyway. And you have no right to come in here and make personal comments like that. Especially not when you are stuffing your face with my chocolate Hobnobs.' By now I was beginning to get really angry. 'I mean, what is it with you lot?' I continued. 'You think you can call on me whenever you want? You think you can disrupt my life day and night and then I'm supposed to feel eternally grateful? Well, I deserve a life as well, you know.'

I stopped. Sven wasn't looking at me. He was looking down. And then I noticed that his shoulders were shaking.

'That's it!' I shouted. 'How dare you sit there and laugh at me!'

Then I saw the light reflecting off the tears on his cheeks and I realised he wasn't laughing. A desperate, dreadful heaving sob burst from his chest.

'Sven...' I said. 'I'm sorry... I didn't realise. What is it? What's wrong?'

He looked up at me, his face smeared with tears.

'My mum...' he sobbed. 'This morning... and I wasn't even there.'

'Oh Sven,' I said. 'I'm so sorry.'

'I didn't have anywhere else to go,' he said. 'I'm sorry, I didn't want to intrude. But I don't have anyone else to talk to.'

'Talk to me,' I said. 'That's what I'm here for.'

So we sat and talked about his mum. She'd been ill for a year. Cancer. There was nothing to say, but then again, I don't think he wanted me to say anything. He just wanted someone to be there for him.

And as we sat and talked, I thought of all the people I would be leaving behind. Glenda and her eco-activism. Aruna and her long words. The bundle of barely-concealed lust that is Vanessa; Andy, blundering around in the world of youth group leadership like a short-sighted bull in a porcelain factory; Giles, torn between heavy metal music and Graham Kendrick; Julian, staring out from the depths of his cagoule, desperate to save the world and achieve martyrdom.

And I wondered who was going to be there for them when they need it? Who was going to mourn with them when they mourn, and laugh with them when they laugh? Who will tell them what they need to know and listen to what they have to say? Who'll challenge them and be challenged by them? Who will live the gospel among them, until they choose to live it for themselves? Who will share his life with them? Who will do any of this, if I don't?

Sven went home a few hours later. We arranged to meet again, over a mug of herbal tea. Maybe I can pick up where we left off. Perhaps out of his depths he will reach up and grasp my hand, and find out that it is really the hand of God.

Later that night I phoned St Thomas's and spoke to the vicar about the job. He was disappointed, but I think he understood. Then I spoke to a few other people here. They all seemed really pleased.

Then I started to unpack.

Cheers
Chris

Lucy and Glenda

From: Chris Francis@Tabernacle.ch.uk

To: Patricia Ryan, P.Ryan@bigplace.com

Subject: A miracle

Pat,

The reaction to my decision to stay was split into three kinds:

1) Genuine pleasure that I was going to be around and a belief that I have made the right decision. (The pastor, most – I am glad to say – of the youth group, some church members, my leadership team.)

2) Total and utter relief that they weren't going to be called on to do any youthwork. (The rest of the church.)

3) A sort of strange delight in that I would still be around to preach at/moan at/generally abuse. (Julian/Stanley the caretaker/the rest of the youth group.)

Anyway, generally speaking, I haven't made this many people happy since I stopped playing the drums in worship services.

The treasurer, Dennis, I have to say, was one of those in group (1) and proved it by sidling up to me after church on Sunday morning with that grin that he usually reserves for when he wants you to sign a covenant form.

'I have some good news for you,' he said.

'You've doubled my wages?'

'No, but we have found you some money to spend.'

Apparently the church is the trustee for a small charitable fund left by one of its church members who pegged out in 1896. In exceptional circumstances (i.e. when he has no choice, or when he is temporarily suffering from generosity) the treasurer can recommend a payout to a worthy cause. This time, I, or rather the youthwork, was it.

'How much?' I asked.

'One thousand,' he said.

There was a pause, during which small lumps of disbelief bounced around the inside of my head.

'You mean yen, presumably,' I said. 'Or pesetas.'

'Pounds, of course,' he replied. 'Use it for whatever you want,' he added hurriedly, 'Except wages.'

So there we are then. Three days back in the job and I have a grand to spend. Naturally I raised it at the youth leaders' meeting, since I felt we all ought to be involved in a mature discussion about our spending priorities.

An argument immediately broke out.

Andy wanted to spend it all on better equipment (i.e. a new pool table). Julian wanted to give it all away on the grounds that he felt I was becoming tainted by 'the love of mammon'.

Aruna wanted to buy a small, but carefully selected library. She even provided a list of recommended theologians, most of whom were German.

My suggestion – which was obviously the best one – was to invest in a DVD player, a home cinema system and a pile of movies. This would be a great resource for the youth group. Someone mentioned the security problems, but that would be easily solved, because all of the equipment would be kept securely in my living room.

Julie suggested that we invest it in training. She had even gone to the lengths of getting some leaflets on courses to train in youth leadership skills. I felt seriously offended.

'I don't need more training,' I said. 'I'm a professional.'

'The difference between an amateur and a professional,' she replied, 'is that a professional never stops learning.'

So there we have it. Even when we do get given money we can't decide what to spend it on. In the end, once our proposals had been slightly modified (no DVD player, but a TV that actually works and a VCR), it boils down to a straight choice – invest in people or invest in equipment. I'm inclined to see Julie's point of view, since it builds for the future, but we need so much now.

So what do we do? Look ahead? Or fix what needs fixing now?

Cheers
Chris

From: Chris Francis@Tabernacle.ch.uk
To: Patricia Ryan, P.Ryan@bigplace.com
Subject: A personal issue

Hi Pat,

OK. You guessed. Yes, Lucy and I are 'an item'.

It all started a couple of months ago when we met, purely by chance, at a friend's party. She had just started coming to church, which annoyed me, because I have this rule about not going out with women from the church where I am working.

Or, I *had* this rule. Because, as you guessed, that's exactly what happened. We just went for a drink and then a meal and then... well, you know how these things progress.

Anyway, the key thing, we both felt, was to take things easy and certainly not to let the other members of the church know about it. So our trips together were mostly taken 'off-patch' – in neighbouring towns where we wouldn't get spotted.

After a while, however, I was beginning to feel like a spy. So we decided to risk a visit to the cinema in Briglimpton.

I thought it would be safe, because the Plaza was showing a French film with subtitles – *La Fromage de Saint Antoine*. Anyway, a pretty safe bet. We were a bit late arriving and joined the queue at the back. As the queue began to move, I heard a familiar voice.

'Fancy seeing you here!' It was the pastor and his wife.

'Oh... er... hello,' I stammered.

'I didn't know you and Lucy were...'

'We're not!' I blurted. 'Definitely not. This is not some kind of relationship but just two friends getting together to go and see a film so don't read anything into it thank you very much.'

There was a pause.

'I was going to say I didn't know you were fans of French films,' said the pastor.

'Oh.'

His wife tugged at his arm.

'Come along George,' she said. 'Let's leave these two young things alone.'

They turned and left.

'We are not young things!' I called after them.

'Speak for yourself,' said Lucy. 'And what do you mean "This is not some kind of relationship"?'

'Sorry,' I replied. 'I just sort of panicked.'

'Well don't worry,' she replied. 'We'll be inside in a minute.'

The queue inched itself forward.

'Well, at least no one else has spotted us – '

It was then that I felt the hairs on the back of my neck stand up. It felt as though someone had filled my spine with ice cold water.

Julian was standing on the steps of the cinema. In his right hand he was holding a banner which read 'Down with French Films!' In his other he was waving a magazine.

'It says in here that this film contains swearing, violence and profanity!' he cried. 'Stay away for the sake of your souls!'

He saw us and at once broke into a happy smile.

'Brother!' he said. 'I didn't know you were going to join the protest! Do you subscribe to *Ban Them All Monthly* as well?' He held up the magazine, which was, apparently, one of the Rev Murdo McBrightly's flagship publications.

'Er, no,' I said.

'Then it was a divine revelation!' he exclaimed. 'A word of God which brought you to join me in my hour of need.'

The queue moved forward. Gradually he realised the truth.

'You're not... going in?' he stammered. 'Have you forgotten your morals? Have you forgotten that you are a pastor of a flock?' And then another thought struck him. 'And is that a woman you are with!' he shouted.

Lucy turned and smiled at him.

'It certainly is,' she said and blew him a kiss.

I think his next phrase contained the words 'scarlet woman' and 'Jezebel', but I'm not sure because Lucy was laughing so loudly.

'I... er... I'm sorry about that,' I said. 'He does get a bit carried away.'

'It's fine,' she said. 'I'm having a wonderful time. Just relax. Anyway, it's all over now.' She took my arm reassuringly. 'Let's get something to eat.'

We wandered, hand in hand, to the refreshment counter and ordered a jumbo carton of popcorn. I took Lucy in my arms and gave her a kiss. It was a magical moment, broken only by the sound of someone dropping a tray of cokes. We turned round.

'Oh,' I said. 'Er, hello Vanessa.'

She was speechless. She just looked at Lucy and then at me and then slowly reached out for some popcorn containers.

Anyway, to cut a long story short, I spoke to the manager afterwards and explained everything, so I think Vanessa will still have a job there if she wants it. The manager did offer to pay for dry-cleaning Lucy's dress.

This morning there were three items in my letterbox; a tract by Murdo McBrightly entitled 'Subtitles: The Sins at the Bottom of the Screen', a photo of myself torn into several pieces and a letter from the pastor saying he had no objection to my dating members of the congregation, but would I try to be a bit more discreet in future?

Oh, and a note from Lucy which simply reads: 'Is it always going to be this much fun?'

Cheers
Chris

From: Chris Francis@Tabernacle.ch.uk
To: Patricia Ryan, P.Ryan@bigplace.com
Subject: Megan

Hi Pat,

Have I told you about Megan yet? Megan joined the group a couple of months ago. She's a nice girl and has made some good friendships already, particularly with Glenda. (In fact, I haven't seen Glenda lately. Megan just said that 'she had a lot on her mind' at the moment. I obviously need to have a chat with her.)

Anyway, Megan came to see me yesterday and we had an interesting conversation.

'I want to talk about worship,' she said.

'Fire away then,' I said.

'Well, it's like this,' she said. 'Why does everyone assume that young people like loud music and jumping around? I'm tired of going to events that assume I'm a hyperactive kangaroo with a hearing impediment. I mean, take the last youth service. It was so loud.'

'Yes, well, that was because Giles broke the knob on the amplifier,' I answered. 'And Vanessa was playing drums and she has a lot of anger to work out at the moment.'

'I think we ought to do a led meditation,' she suggested. 'Something quiet and contemplative.'

I was positively enthusiastic. The words 'quiet' and 'contemplative' and 'youth group' are an enticing – if unlikely – combination. So I suggested that at the next youth group, she lead us in a meditation.

'I spent some time last year on retreat in Scotland,' she said. 'It was an Ignatian Reflection led by Sister Gertrude Assumpta. She's one of the Nuns of the Perpetual Ablutions.'

'She must be a bit washed out,' I said.

She looked sternly at me. 'I hope you are going to take this seriously,' she said. 'They are very devout ladies. They call themselves "The Washers of the World".'

Anyway, last night we met up and I told everyone that Megan was going to lead us in a meditation. We all closed our eyes, and Megan started to speak.

'Let us close our eyes and be still and prepare to cleanse our innermost beings. First, let us consider the dishcloth. It is not proud. It washes the fine glass and the dirty mug. It is humble and pure. And you can buy it in packs of five. Is God speaking to us through the dishcloth?'

I sneaked a look. Most people were looking more confused than anything else. She continued...

'Let us consider the flannel. It washes the face, the arms and... other bits. It cleanses the dirt and the filth. Are we, like the flannel, prepared to go into the dark? What does God say to us through the flannel?'

From my left came the sound of a muffled snort. Andy was evidently considering his dark places.

'Let us consider the sponge. It holds water and releases it when squeezed. Do we, like the sponge, release the cleansing water when we are squeezed? Do we allow God to make us more spongy?'

Andy was now shaking with suppressed laughter. I had the feeling that he was certainly about to release something.

'Let us consider the loofah. Long and thin and sitting in the corner of the bath. Helping others to reach the parts they cannot reach on their own. Going around the back of our world and giving it a good scratch. Is God speaking to us through the loofah?'

At this point Andy left the room. He was crying. As he went, I heard Julian whisper to Megan, 'Did you say loofah or Luther?' and all of a sudden it was too much.

'I... er... I'll just go and see if he's all right,' I said to Megan. 'It's obviously been deeply moving.'

As I closed the door behind me, I heard the words 'Let us consider the pumice stone...'

Cheers
Chris

PS: Glenda's just phoned. Seemed very upset, but wouldn't tell me what it was over the phone. I asked Julie to give her a call. I expect it's nothing. She's probably getting upset about the ozone layer again, you know what she's like. The last time Glenda phoned me 'in crisis' it was because she had just watched a documentary on the plight of the North American Spotted Owl and couldn't understand why it was being hunted. My suggestion that 'it probably tastes good' did not go down well.

From: Chris Francis@Tabernacle.ch.uk
To: Patricia Ryan, P.Ryan@bigplace.com
Subject: Urgent prayer!

Pat,

Julie called round this morning. The reason Glenda wasn't at the meeting last night is that she's pregnant! Apparently, she told Megan last week, but no one else knows yet.

Anyway, I went round this evening to have a chat with Glenda and her parents – two nice church members who wear matching cardigans and who are in a state of complete shock at what has happened to their daughter.

It wasn't a comfortable meeting – I had a strange feeling that they held me somehow responsible for Glenda's pregnancy. Not *directly* responsible, of course, but the implication was that there was something wrong with my work if one of *my* young people could get pregnant. (And maybe I feel this as well – I'm trying to look at it more objectively, but I can't help feeling a failure myself.)

So it wasn't long before the recriminations started to fly with Glenda and her parents flinging accusations at each other and me caught in the middle.

'What is everyone going to think!' said her mum. 'You've ruined your life!'

'Don't say that!' said Glenda.

'Well, it's true!'

'I know it is! You think I don't know that?'

I felt like I needed one of those blue UN hats. And possibly an Armalite rifle to go with it.

Suddenly, the doorbell rang. We all froze. Her dad answered the door and I heard, with a certain sinking of my heart, the unmistakable tones of Julian.

'I have just heard of your time of travail, Mr Hogarth,' he said. 'And I have come round in a spirit of humility and Christian morality.'

'Don't let him in!' hissed Glenda to me. 'He's probably come to stone me!'

But, as anyone who has been the recipient of Julian's doorstep evangelism knows, he is an unstoppable force.

'It's a bit inconvenient right now...' began Glenda's dad.

'There is never an inconvenient time for the Lord's work,' said Julian and before we knew it, his cagoule-clad figure swept into the room.

Glenda looked up at him.

'Hello,' she said. 'I expect you've brought me a tract or something, have you? Or have you come to cast me out?'

'No,' said Julian. 'I came to bring you this.'

And he reached into his bag and pulled out a teddy-bear.

Cheers
Chris

From: Chris Francis@Tabernacle.ch.uk
To: Patricia Ryan, P.Ryan@bigplace.com
Subject: The day off

Hi Pat,

Thanks for the card, but I'm fine, really. As you can see, I'm back at home now – I was only in overnight, for 'observation'.

You ask how it all happened. Well, it was a combination of things, really. I'd had loads of stuff over the New Year and into the last few months, so I'd been working pretty much seven days a week. Everywhere I turned there were meetings to attend, groups to speak to, plans to be finalised, phone calls to make – I had a diary so huge it made *War and Peace* look like a post-it note. Even worse, Lucy was away working in the States, so I had nothing to divert me.

But Thursday was free. That was what I kept telling myself – 'Thursday was my day off'. And by Wednesday evening I needed it. The morning saw me taking the school assembly and some lessons; in the afternoon I had a meeting with the pastor. Early evening my sister dropped in, bringing with her my three-year-old niece Kensington (she has an older sister called Chelsea) and I gave her a toy doctor's kit for her birthday. Later in the evening there was a planning group. By the time I fell into bed on Wednesday night, I was completely exhausted. Still, I knew one thing: 'Thursday was free.' I would start with a lie-in...

The alarm went off at 6:30 a.m. Like a fool, I'd been so tired that I'd forgotten to reset it. I was almost back to sleep when next door's car alarm started howling. This is the most sensitive car alarm in the world. So by 7:00 I was wide awake. I went downstairs and noticed that Kensington had left behind some of her toy doctor's bag. I was just collecting up the bits she'd left behind when the doorbell rang.

Julian was on the doorstep. On seeing me he looked shocked.

'I... er... came to give you this,' he muttered, thrusting my Bible at me. 'You left it at my house...' He stared at me.

'Oh thanks,' I said. 'I'm always forgetting things at the moment. Tell the truth, these days I feel like I'm out of my head.'

He looked very serious. 'I shall be praying for you, brother,' he whispered.

I closed the door, wondering why he'd looked so shocked. Then I caught sight of myself in the mirror; gaunt, unshaven, hair all over the place, bags under my eyes. And holding a syringe. I flung open the door, prepared to chase Julian down the road to explain it was only my niece's toy, but he had gone. 'Terrific,' I thought. 'He already thinks I'm an infidel. Now he thinks I'm a junkie as well.'

It took till after lunch until I had calmed down. Lunch was real comfort food – bangers and mash, with sausages from the butchers round the corner. After that I felt in a good mood again and settled down for a snooze on the sofa. The doorbell rang. I ignored it, but whoever it was started to hammer on the door as well.

'Yes?' I snapped, wrenching the door open. It was the pastor.

'I just called to remind you that today is your day off,' he said. There was a pause while I tried to come to terms with what was happening.

'I know...' I began to say.

'So make sure you get your rest,' he said.

'But I was just...' I stuttered.

'If I were you,' he said, 'I'd have a lie down on the sofa and go to sleep.' And with that, he turned round and zoomed off on his moped.

'THANKS FOR YOUR HELP!' I yelled at the retreating figure. I was so furious I slammed the door shut. Stupid mistake. You should always go *inside* before slamming the door shut. That way, you won't get locked out, will you?

I eventually got back in with a spare key from the neighbours and headed straight to the couch. I unplugged the phone and, just to make sure, disconnected the wires from the doorbell. Then, I made another stupid mistake. The room felt stuffy and close, so I opened a window to let some air in.

'Hi there,' said Sven, peering through the curtains. 'Mind if I climb aboard?'

What could I say?

'Sorry to barge in on you,' he said. 'Just needed to talk. You know how it is.'

'Yes,' I said wearily, 'I know how it is.'

We talked for a bit and then he suggested going out for a meal. I felt that a bit of fresh air would do me good, so we made our way down to the Management Consultant's Arms. (It used to be the Bricklayer's Arms, but the landlord decided he wanted to go for a more up-market clientele.)

I was halfway through my Biryani when the world started spinning. I started to feel terribly sick.

'Are you all right?' he said.

I just about made it outside the front door of the pub when I was horribly, violently sick.

That was bad enough, but worse was to follow.

'Oh that it should come to this!' said a familiar voice as I lay on the pavement. 'First the drugs, now the demon drink!'

'No, it's not what it looks like!' I protested. 'I'm not well.'

But it was too late. And the last thing I remember is Julian's face, locked in concerned prayer, before I passed out.

The doctors say it was a combination of exhaustion and food poisoning, probably brought on by eating out-of-date sausages. I think it's the stress of this job and the never-ending demands. Julian thinks its drink, drugs and debauchery. One of us is right. I wonder who?

Cheers
Chris

From: Chris Francis@Tabernacle.ch.uk
To: Patricia Ryan, P.Ryan@bigplace.com
Subject: That old nagging feeling...

Hi Pat,

For the last few days I've had this strange feeling of impending doom.

I don't know what it is. I thought at first it was just because Julian was going through one of his ultra-holy spells. On Sunday morning I was talking to Aruna and Vanessa – they were all fired up about organising a prayer and fund-raising meeting for some disaster victims. I thought this was a good idea – for one thing it would get Aruna involved in actually doing something. She's very good at discussing things; she could theorise for Britain – but I think she needs to do a bit less thinking and more acting. Anyway, all this was running through my mind as I talked to them, but I couldn't take it any further because I suddenly heard a yell. Julian had fallen into the duck pond on the green in front of the church. I rushed to his rescue. Apparently he had been trying to test his faith by walking on water.

After that things got a bit chaotic. Stanley came out and started complaining about 'abuse of the local facilities' by young people.

Anyway, after all that, I had this nagging feeling that somehow I had forgotten something, something very important. So on Wednesday I checked my diary and did all that I had to. I sent in my amended budget to the treasurer, and photocopied all the stuff for the weekend. I even started to prepare some new school assemblies I've got to do. I sorted through the post with my usual method: anything in a plain brown envelope gets carefully filed in the pile of unwanted junk mail. Then at five o'clock, Lucy phoned me up.

'Anything happening tomorrow?' she asked.

'Not that I know of,' I replied. 'It's my day off.'

'Good,' she replied. 'Grab your passport, pack a bag and be ready and waiting.'

It transpired she'd won two tickets on the Eurostar. So we hopped on, and went to stay with her brother, who works in Bruges. I don't know what he does, but he earns a lot of money – enough to take us out for a great meal. The next day we did some sightseeing and some shopping before coming back late in the evening. It had been a wonderful time and just what I needed – a complete mini-break from church, the young people and all the stresses and strains.

It was only when I stepped through the front door that the old feeling returned. And then I saw it: the answerphone was lit up like the control panel at NASA. Number of messages: too many to count.

I pressed the button. The dull voice of the answerphone said, 'First recorded message':

'Hi Chris, it's Julie here. Um... I don't know if you've forgotten that we were supposed to be having a special prayer meeting at Vanessa's house tonight? Only she's prepared a meal and everything. I expect you're on your way... see you.'

Beep. Next message:

'Chris? Andy. I'm at Vanessa's. We've started without you. If there's a problem let me know and I'll come and fetch you.'

Beep. Next message:

'Hello Chris, it's Glenda speaking. Vanessa's a bit upset now. She was really hoping you'd be here. You know what she's like. Could you come as soon as possible. Hang on... no, Julian, don't go near her...'

Beep. Next message:

'Greetings. Julian here. I am being persecuted. I told Vanessa that she was being an undisciplined Christian and she threw a large trifle over me. She may be possessed. Come at once.'

Beep. Next message:

'Hi Chris, it's Aruna here. Look, I know you're really busy and really important and really everything, but I do think you might have turned up tonight. Vanessa and I put a lot of work into it. Call me.' (Long sarcasm-drenched pause) 'If you've got the time.'

Beep. Next message:

'Hello Chris, it's Vanessa. I'm sorry I got so upset, I'm sure you have a good reason for missing the meeting, don't worry I forgive you. I'm sure you were out working for the Lord in some dangerous and difficult mission field.' (Menacingly) 'I'm sure you weren't just off with your girlfriend.'

And so it went on. And then it hit me. That was what I'd been talking to Aruna and Vanessa about when I was called away to rescue Julian. I dimly recall saying something stupid and youth-workery like 'Great idea, let's do it!' but I didn't know they'd actually organised anything. Unless, of course they'd sent a note through. A note in a plain brown envelope. A note which I'd picked up and put with the junk mail.

Oh stuff it.

So. Now I have to explain to Aruna that I'd missed the first event she'd ever organised because I didn't read her letter. And I have to explain to

Vanessa that, yes, I did indeed spend the evening with the woman she views as her hated rival. And I have to pay Julian's dry-cleaning bill.

Any ideas on how to proceed?

Cheers
Chris

From: Chris Francis@Tabernacle.ch.uk
To: Patricia Ryan, P.Ryan@bigplace.com
Subject: Congratulations... sort of

Pat,

Thanks for your congratulations – I'm a bit amazed myself. I thought Lucy had more common sense than to agree to marry me, but there you go, love does strange things to us all.

Anyway, after letting my family and close friends know, the next step was to tell the youth group. Obviously there were some sensitive issues here – most notably telling Vanessa, a girl who doesn't so much carry a torch for me, as wield a flipping great flame thrower. And then there was the pastor and everyone else. Anyway, here's how it went.

>> Conversation 1: Me and Vanessa

Me: Vanessa, you know that Lucy and I have been going out for some time now.

Vanessa: I know Chris and it's fine by me. Honestly.

Me: Really?

Vanessa: Oh yes. I've had counselling about it and I'm fine.

Me: Well that's great.

Vanessa: Of course, if you got engaged or anything like that then probably I wouldn't be fine at all.

Me: Oh...

Vanessa: Because when my counsellor suggested that to me the other day I couldn't stop crying for ages and I went really hysterical and everything.

Me: Oh.

Vanessa: So what was it you called to tell me?

Me: (Long pause) Oh, nothing....

>> Conversation 2: Me and the pastor

Me: Hi George, just calling to let you know some good news. Lucy and I are engaged.

Pastor: That's great! Congratulations and blessings on you both. Let me know the date and I'll book it in straightaway.

Me: Er....

Pastor: No, don't thank me. It will be an honour to preach at the service. I have an excellent three hour message on 'The Concept of Headship as Outlined in Paul's Letter to the Ephesians'. Blessings!

>> Conversation 3: Me and the church treasurer

Treasurer: Congratulations. She works full-time, doesn't she?

Me: Er... yes.

Treasurer: I was just wondering if we can make an adjustment to your salary...

Me: (Menacingly) Not if you don't want me to make an adjustment to your face.

>> Conversation 4: Me and Vanessa (Again)

Me: Vanessa, the thing is that Lucy and I are...

Vanessa: You're splitting up? You're finished? Oh I knew this would happen!

Me: No, you see...

Vanessa: (Recovering) Not that it worries me of course. Couldn't care less, really. Got to go. (Puts phone down)

>> Conversation 5: Me and Julian

Julian: Congratulations. About time. For someone in your position it has been obvious that the sins of the flesh have been gnawing at your soul for some time now.

Me: Have they?

Julian: Oh yes. I discerned it. That's why I gave you that pamphlet by the Rev Murdo McBrightly – 'Conquering Carnality in the Clergy'. Have you read it?

>> Conversation 6: Me and the church secretary

Secretary: Many congratulations, Chris. And, of course, the church will be greatly blessed by Lucy's ministry.

Me: She hasn't got a ministry. It's one of the things I like about her.

Secretary: Don't be silly. As your wife she'll be the deputy youthworker by default. Will you tell her, or shall I?

Me: Oh, I think it would be far better coming from you. And put her down for the Chair of the Tabernacle Wives Fellowship while you're at it won't you?

Secretary: Good idea.

>> Conversation 7: Me and Stanley

Me: Just thought you might like to know that Lucy and I are getting married.

Stanley: No confetti. You hear me? No confetti. It clogs the drains.

>> Conversation 8: Me and Glenda

Me: I'm marrying Lucy.

Glenda: Are you? That's funny because Vanessa just told me you were splitting up. Congrats anyway. I trust it will be a green wedding.

Me: Thanks. Listen... er... Glenda. You know that pastoral sensitivity course that I went on a few weeks back.

Glenda: Yes.

Me: You know how I particularly chose the module on 'Telling it like it is: Being Pastorally Butch'?

Glenda: Yes.

Me: You couldn't tell Vanessa could you?

Cheers
Chris

From: Chris Francis@Tabernacle.ch.uk
To: Patricia Ryan, P.Ryan@bigplace.com
Subject: Agnes

Hi Pat,

Something incredible happened this week: Agnes Miller died.

Not that Agnes' death was incredible. She was ninety-three after all, and she hadn't been very well for a while. No, what was incredible was the effect it had.

Let me explain. Agnes was one of those ladies – and you don't get many nowadays – who lived for mission. Her parents were missionaries in China and her brother, Ernest, spent many years working with a missionary society called 'Regions Behind', which, I believe, worked in Africa. Back here in Briglimpton, Agnes talked about, supported, prayed for and generally enthused about mission from dawn to dusk. For years she was the church missionary secretary and, given 30 seconds, she would corner any member of the congregation, young or old, and regale them with tales of the latest opportunities overseas.

So I wasn't too sad to hear of her departure. She knew where she was going and who she was going to be with. But what was amazing was the effect it had on the youth group. I came home one afternoon to find a load of them standing on my doorstep. They were quiet and subdued.

I opened the door and they trooped into the lounge, like a load of depressed sheep.

'What are you lot looking so sad about?' I said.

'It's Agnes,' said Vanessa. 'We just heard.'

'Oh,' I replied, somewhat surprised. 'Did you know her well, then?'

And then all the stories came out. Vanessa had grown up with the old lady. Agnes had been her first teacher in Sunday school.

'She was the first person to give me a Bible,' she said.

Julian had, completely unknown to me, been meeting with Agnes once a week for the past few years to pray for missionary work throughout the world.

'She was a very godly lady,' he said. 'I would give her my tracts to read and she would read them. Unlike some people,' he added, looking at me rather pointedly.

Glenda, who was sitting quietly in the corner, said: 'She had me round for tea after she heard about me being pregnant. She'd knitted a woolly caterpillar for the baby. At least, I think it was a caterpillar. It could have been a tiger. She wasn't very good at knitting by then.'

Andy was looking gloomy.

'And how did you know her, Andy?' I asked.

'She converted me,' he said.

I had to do a quick mental double take. It was hard to put the frail old lady and the grubby, dishevelled car mechanic together in the same frame.

'Er... are we talking about the same woman?'

'Of course. It was after a church service a few years ago. I only went because it was raining and I was bored. She came up and spoke to me afterwards. She gave me a cup of coffee. Anyway, one thing led to another and by the time I left the church that evening I was a Christian.'

As we talked, it became clear that this little old lady had had an effect on the lives of these young people that I'd never imagined.

'Well, I'm amazed,' I said. 'I would never have dreamed that you and she would have had anything to do with one another.'

Glenda looked at me.

'She liked us,' she said. 'It was as simple as that.'

'You're just like the rest of them,' said Andy. 'You pigeonhole people. The church puts one lot of people in the box marked "old" and another lot of people in the box marked "young" and doesn't expect anything of them or believe they have much to offer. But people have a lot to offer. If they're given the chance.'

He was right of course. As we sat there I remembered my own conversations with Agnes, when I first came to the church, and how she understood something fundamental about youthwork – that it is a missionary activity. That it involves reaching out to, befriending, communicating with and living among a different culture.

The truth is, Andy was right. I have been looking for volunteers for the youthwork, but only certain types of volunteers. People who I classified as 'relevant' or 'understanding' or 'young enough'. But who are we to say who is too old to be a youthworker? Agnes liked young people. Agnes cared about young people. That seemed to be qualification enough.

Cheers
Chris

PS: I've just had a phone call from the solicitors handling Agnes' estate. It seems she really did care about young people. So much so that she's left the youth group quite a lot of money in her will.

The only snag is, we've got to go overseas to get it.

I'll tell you more later...

From: Chris Francis@Tabernacle.ch.uk
To: Patricia Ryan, P.Ryan@bigplace.com
Subject: The call of the Mission Field

Hi Pat,

You know, every now and then, something amazing happens. A cloud has a silver lining. A piece of glass turns into a rough diamond. A flower blooms on the compost heap of life.

Sorry, but I'm feeling lyrical. I told you last time about Agnes Miller, the old lady who died and left the youth group a substantial sum of money in her will?

Just moments after the letter from the solicitors dropped through the letter box, the church treasurer was on the doorstep. I swear that man can smell money.

'I've found the best account to put it in,' he announced. 'It offers the highest rates of interest, as long as you don't make any withdrawals for 13 years.'

'Are you kidding?' I said. 'I'm not going to put it away. I'm going to spend it.'

He went pale and had to sit down.

'Spend it?' he whispered. 'Spend it?'

'Yes. In fact I have to.'

I showed him the letter from Messrs Sponge, Freebie and Mastadon, solicitors for the estate of the late Agnes Miller.

'You see that clause down the bottom,' I said. 'We can only use the money for one thing. We have to use the money to give the young people missionary experience. Overseas.'

He looked up at me.

'You can't take them overseas,' he said. 'Not that lot. It would constitute an act of war.'

But there was nothing he could do about it. Agnes' will was quite specific. As she had spent so much of her life as a missionary, she wanted to give the young people some experience of overseas service. The money had to be spent in taking them on mission abroad.

I decided to ask the youth group for suggestions as to possible projects and destinations, in accordance with my deeply held principles of consultation and empowerment.

'I believe the Rev Murdo McBrightly has an emerging ministry somewhere up the Ganges,' said Julian.

'I think we should go on a study trip to visit some of the archaeological digs looking at Ancient Mesopotamian kingdoms,' suggested Aruna. 'It's fascinating what they're revealing about the Hittite civilisation.'

'In what way is that mission work?' said Julian. 'It's well known, archaeology is a tool of the devil. I've got a pamphlet about it by the Reverend Murdo McBrightly entitled, 'Satan's Spadework: *Time Team* versus Eternal Faith'.

'It's called thinking for yourself,' replied Aruna. 'Something I doubt is encouraged by your stupid Reverend McThingy...'

'Now, now, kiddies,' said Andy. 'I think we should do our own thing. What about some outreach to the bars and clubs around Malaga?'

'You just want to go dancing!' said Glenda.

I decided to completely abandon my deeply held principles of consultation and empowerment.

'This is getting us nowhere,' I said. 'If you can't decide yourselves, I'll have to decide something for you.'

Then Giles spoke up. He'd been quite quiet up till now.

'I've got some friends who run an orphanage in Romania,' he said. 'They're always looking for people to help them. Maybe we could go there.'

And that's what we're going to do. Later this summer, I, accompanied by members of the youth group, will be going to Romania to spend ten days working alongside a local church.

I told Lucy about the final details.

'It's an immensely poor area and there's a lot of hardship and deprivation,' I said.

She looked at me.

'And are you going to take your youth group visiting these poor people?'

'Yes.'

'Chris,' she said. 'Haven't they suffered enough?'

She can laugh.

Wait till she finds out that she's coming too.

Cheers

Chris

From: Chris Francis@Tabernacle.ch.uk
To: Patricia Ryan, P.Ryan@bigplace.com
Subject: Raising support

Hi Pat,

What always amazes me about young people is how much energy there is in there, just waiting to be let out.

I mean, most of the time, my lot mooch around in that kind of semi-zombie state which affects us all in adolescence. Everything is a sort of slump. They walk slumped, sit slumped, and even think in a slump. But find an idea that excites them and it's like a minor explosion. Suddenly they rush around doing things you never believed them capable of.

Take our overseas trip to Romania. As things have worked out, about twelve of the youth group will be going with me and Lucy to Romania. The money from Agnes Miller's legacy will pay for half their trip – they have to raise the other half of the cost. I didn't want any holidaymakers on this trip.

And it's amazing the energy that's been released and the sacrifices that have been made. Julian is doing a sponsored preach (although mercifully not on a Sunday, so we don't have to sit and listen to him.) Andy, confounding all my gender expectations, has taken in the washing and ironing for most of the church. He is charging 15 quid a load, washed and ironed. This seemed to me to offer remarkable value for money, so I took him my backlog of dirty laundry which runs back to, at a guess, 2001. His face went a horrible shade of white when he saw it, but he needed the money.

Vanessa, meanwhile, went to a car boot sale and sold off some of her huge collection of romantic fiction. When I saw how much she'd raised, I was amazed.

'You've done fantastically for a car boot sale!' I said.

'Oh, I didn't only sell them there,' she admitted. 'Some of them I sold at auction at Sothebys.'

'You what?' I said.

'I had some rare first editions,' she replied. 'My signed first edition of Letitia Femulen's *Love in a Tight Bodice* went for 60 quid.'

'Are you sure you want to sell all these treasured possessions?'

'Oh yes,' she said. 'Anyway, I've got four first editions of that one.'

And here's another amazing thing. The group who wanted to go decided to pool all the money they raised and to spread it equally. This means those who couldn't raise as much money could still join us.

We are going to a little Romanian town called Rubba Balûn. Not exactly a tourist centre, unless you really want to visit a 1970s carbon manufacturing plant and an old coal mine. Times are tough, the people have little money and the traditional industries are declining. We are going out to help build a church – *literally* build a church, because the old one fell down during a minor earthquake last year.

At first I thought just we were going, but yesterday I had a call from Geoff Rumsden, owner of the local builders merchants and member of the congregation.

'All right,' he said. 'Tell him I'll do it. And a few of my workmen will come with me. But I don't want any more of those flipping leaflets.'

'Er…' I replied. 'Tell who you'll do what? And what leaflets are you on about?'

'Julian!' he exclaimed. 'He's been round here every day for the last week persuading me to take a lorry load of building materials out to that town of yours. And when he wasn't here in person he was pushing leaflets through the door. I've got one here – it's called 'Overcoming Selfishness – The Delights of the Donating Life'. It's by Murdo somebody.'

I sighed. 'Well, don't worry, I'll tell him. And thanks very much.'

I put the phone down, amazed. When Julian gets going there is no stopping him. I think, before we go I will have to check with the Foreign Office about whether we need a special export licence for Julian.

Technically, he's a dangerous weapon.

Cheers
Chris

From: Chris Francis@Tabernacle.ch.uk
To: Patricia Ryan, P.Ryan@bigplace.com
Subject: Back from Romania

Hi Pat

Here, for your eyes only, is my diary of our Romania trip. I couldn't email this to you at the time, but perhaps that's just as well.

DAY ONE

We arrived late last night after a long journey. The flight was OK, apart from a slight delay at the airport while Julian went up and down the plane casting out what he called a 'spirit of heaviness.'

We eventually arrived in the town at about 9 p.m. When they invented the phrase 'run-down' they must have had this place in mind. Rubba Balûn is a small mining town. Now, like so much of this country, it is fighting against decay and poverty and lack of supplies. Water and electricity is a luxury. Hope is a necessity.

We were met on arrival by the pastor, Laszlo, who took us into the old church. Well, I say 'church'. It was really a collection of bricks stacked into a kind of rectangle shape. With a pulpit at one end. The walls were only standing upright out of habit.

'As you can see,' said Laszlo, 'It needs some work.'

'Laszlo,' I said. 'It's falling apart.'

'Oh no,' he said. 'It's not that bad.' He patted one of the walls affectionately and a brick near the roof fell out. 'Anyway,' he said, 'you will soon get used to it. And it will keep you cool at night.'

It was then that I realised that this was not only the building we were going to be renovating, it was the building where we would be staying. We were going to be living on the building site.

We were all absolutely exhausted and slept well. Well, apart from a strange dream I had. I sat up in bed and looked around me. The old church was filled with an eerie moonlight. And for a moment I had the strangest feeling that someone was talking. And I swore I could make out the shape of something in the pulpit – someone talking. Anyway, the noise stopped and I fell back to sleep and forgot all about it.

DAY TWO

Organised by Geoff Rumsden, who had arrived with his lorry full of materials, we started work rebuilding the church. Geoff formed us all into teams, the only problem being Julian, who was supposed to be repairing the roof with me and Andy.

'I don't have the gift of exterior woodwork,' he said.

'That one must have passed me by,' I said.

'Oh you must have read it,' said Andy. 'Some are called to be teachers, some preachers, some exterior woodworkers...'

'You can mock,' said Julian, 'but I should be using my unique skills.'

'And what are they, Julian?' I asked.

He paused.

'I could exhort you.'

'I'm sorry?'

'You know, like in Nehemiah. He exhorted the people to rebuild the walls of Jerusalem. I was reading it last night in my Bible.'

'Julian,' I said. 'The chemical toilet is going to need emptying soon. Perhaps you would like to do that instead?'

I have never seen anyone go up a ladder so fast. I must be good at this exhorting business.

DAY THREE

Another great day. I was up on the roof again with Andy and Julian and we made good progress. (Luckily, it's a big, flat roof so I can easily cope with the height!) Although I have to say I don't think much of their technique! Still I managed to pull things together. In the evening we had a great time of worship with the local church here. They are wonderful people who have endured so much.

I had that dream again last night.

DAY FOUR

Today was still thrilling, although I have to admit that I began to wonder just what Geoff Rumsden was doing. I mean, no one actually appointed him leader, did they? Just because he's a builder...

Anyway, naturally I haven't said anything. And although it was manifestly unfair that I should spend another day on top of the roof – especially given my fear of heights – I just carried on. Andy didn't help. Honestly I thought he was a trained mechanic, but the way he handles a hammer! I tried to show him the right way but he just grunted.

'Learn a lot about carpentry at Bible College, did you?' he said.

I informed him that actually, before I became a youthworker, I was almost a carpenter. Or at least I worked at B&Q during the holidays, which was much the same thing. There was no getting through to him. You just can't teach some people.

Dreamt about the figure in the pulpit again. Perhaps it's the sleeping bag. Julian had persuaded the local army surplus store to kit us out with sleeping bags. Which would be fine except that they are, apparently, 'arctic strength' and come with a zip-up hood and more padding than a three-piece suite. I am sure that this is making me too hot.

DAY FIVE

I have swapped teams. I had a word with Geoff and he saw the point that someone else ought to be on the roof to allow me to exercise more 'hands on' control down at ground level. He wasn't exactly gracious about it, but there you go. Perhaps he is not as spiritually mature as I am.

In the afternoon I decided that we all needed a break, so I said that tomorrow we would have a day off and go sight-seeing in the mountains. To be honest I felt that we needed something. There has been some muttering reaching my ears about various members of the group.

Even I have been affected. Andy is beginning to get on my nerves. Instead of supporting my attempts to keep tabs on things and check on progress, he keeps whistling the theme tune from *Ground Force* whenever I come near. Now my sense of humour is as good as anyone's, but it does get a bit wearing in the end.

Anyway, tomorrow will bring us back together.

DAY SIX

It wasn't my fault. Obviously the map was completely wrong. I blame Laszlo. The place where he said he would meet us with the food for the barbecue was in a completely different direction. The man is a fool. Anyway I do not know what they are complaining about. A 14-hour hike is nothing. They'd have to do it all the time if they were in the SAS.

Laszlo is just one of many incompetent people. Geoff obviously knows nothing about building. How I could ever have appointed Andy as my assistant I'll never know. All he is good at is sarcasm. The girls spend all their time giggling and are utterly useless at all manual work. Julian is a creature from another planet. If he mentions Nehemiah one more time I will 'exhort' him with a mallet.

Even Lucy has lost some of her charms. She is so perpetually, infuriatingly optimistic all the time. Even when – due entirely to that stupid map – we wound up crossing the same bridge four times, she kept smiling.

I am not sleeping well. Last night the dream figure in the pulpit was singing 'Jesus wants me for a Sunbeam'. More of a nightmare really.

DAY SEVEN

There is a lot of tension in the camp. Some teams are hardly on speaking terms. I caught Andy earlier trying to throw Julian out of a ground floor window. I remonstrated with him. It wasn't that I was worried about Julian, but I didn't want him landing in the middle of the concrete we'd just laid.

We had a prayer and praise time tonight. There was a notable lack of enthusiasm. (And, indeed, a notable lack of prayer and praise.)

I spoke to Lucy over the quality of some of the girls' work and she just laughed at me. Then she looked at me and asked if I was feeling OK.

I'm just tired, that's all. Team-work would be so easy if everyone else weren't such idiots. It's a tremendous strain leading this team and it's taking it out of me. Especially when every night is wrecked by mysterious dream sermons.

DAY EIGHT

Toil. Grind. Irritation. But at least the work is nearly finished.

The figure was there again in my dreams. Hooded like a monk, it stands in the pulpit and drones in a weird voice. Every now and then I make out a familiar word, but mostly it is just a blur. I wonder what it means?

DAY NINE

It all sorted itself out on the roof. I had just spent two hours with some of the men from the church moving the old pulpit. Moving the wooden pulpit was no problem, but try as we might we couldn't budge the old cast-iron steps that led up to it, and now they stood there, all alone, leading nowhere. For a moment I thought they were a symbol of this trip. A lot of steps leading nowhere, but my musings were interrupted by Geoff who shouted at me that I was needed up on the roof. I thought about arguing, but decided it was easier just to do it. I propped the steps up with some spare bags of concrete and headed out to climb the ladder. When I arrived on the roof, there was Laszlo waiting for me.

'Good!' he exclaimed. 'You should be the one to do this.'

And I saw that he was holding a cross.

'This was on the church before the earthquake tore it down last year,' he said. 'I want you to be the one to help me put it back.'

I saw that someone – Geoff probably – had already been up here arranging the fittings. All we had to do was lift it and put it in. And as I looked at Laszlo, holding it aloft and inviting me to come and help him, it was as if I was seeing the shape for the first time. Two simple lines. One reaching out, one reaching upwards. The ultimate symbol of sacrifice and love and servanthood. And I realised what an idiot I'd been.

'I can't do it, Laszlo,' I said. 'I've spent days feeling miserable and moody and selfish and trying to be the leader. I have no right...'

He held up a hand.

'Who has the right to raise the cross?' he said. 'None of us are worthy, but all of us should do it. It is what we are here to do. To lift this thing as high as we can.'

So together he and I lifted the wooden cross and placed it into the socket. It stood at the highest point of the church, a symbol, a beacon, a living challenge. From below there was cheering – and there they all were, the townsfolk and the young people together applauding and cheering and waving. I felt so proud of everyone who had worked so hard, and so ashamed of myself.

'Look at them,' said Laszlo. 'They have learned so much. We have learned from them. And it is all thanks to you.'

'What have you learned from us?'

He smiled. 'Friendship,' he said. 'We learned what it means to be friends.'

DAY TEN

It was the noise which woke me. A huge, groaning creaking sound, a raised voice and then a crash. I sat up and there, at the other end of the church the moonlight poured in to show a cloud, and in the cloud a strange, wild figure.

'What's happening!' said Andy.

'It's the hooded preacher!' I said, pointing. 'Look!'

It stood in the midst of a white cloud, moaning slightly. A strange, unearthly shape, like a giant slug or caterpillar, yet with a head and mouth. And then I realised that it was speaking.

'Don't be afraid!' he was saying. 'Remember the Lord! Fight for your friends, your families and your homes!'

Andy rubbed his eyes.

'Oi, Julian,' he said. 'Why don't you shut up and get some sleep, eh?'

The figure shook itself and looked around it.

'How...' it stuttered. 'How did I get here?'

And so, the mystery is solved. Every night Julian, still clad in his sleeping bag, has been shuffling to the end of the church, climbing the steps into the old pulpit and reciting passages from Nehemiah. And he never woke once. He has been sleep-preaching.

Only tonight there was no pulpit at the end of the steps and he fell into the concrete bags below. He didn't seem at all hurt by the experience.

Maybe the fact that he was asleep meant that his body just bounced.

'Nehemiah,' I said. 'Go back to bed. We've got a long journey ahead of us. You've done a good job, but now, I think we all need some rest.'

Cheers
Chris

From: Chris Francis@Tabernacle.ch.uk
To: Patricia Ryan, P.Ryan@bigplace.com
Subject: 'Vivacious Vanessa'

Hi Pat

Well, it's been an interesting time in the youth group since returning from Romania. There has been a real buzz about the place.

The main problem I've had is trying to ensure that those who went don't alienate those who stayed behind. For days it was all they talked about and every meeting was full of 'do you remember...' and 'what about the time we...' It was only when one of the youth group who didn't go because of other commitments, rather angrily stood up in the middle of one meeting and asked why we didn't all stay there if the place was so wonderful that I realised we might have been letting our enthusiasm run away with us.

Nevertheless, the trip has had one unfortunate side effect, following coverage in the local press. The local newspapers ran several stories on the trip. The rather sedate *Briglimpton Argus* had a picture of the youth group and the caption 'Church youngsters visit quite interesting place'. I would quote the story but it was so boring I lost interest after the third paragraph.

However, it was the *Briglimpton Star* – our local tabloid – which really put the cat among the pigeons. They used the same picture, but managed to crop out everyone except Vanessa and ran the headline 'Vivacious Vanessa's Mercy Mission'. Here's the article

Vivacious Vanessa Bodie (17) is my idea of a missionary! This local beauty has just come back from Romania where she has been warming the hearts of poor people. Vanessa, who lists her ambitions as 'to run my own hairdressing salon and achieve world peace' is no Mother Teresa.

'I'm no nun,' she said, saucily.

The *Star* says she can minister to us any time!

I phoned Vanessa up afterwards to commiserate with her, but she seemed rather upbeat about it. 'I thought it was rather a good picture, actually,' she said.

'But it made you look like a complete bimbo!' I said. 'And what was all that "nun" business?'

'Well the reporter asked me if I was a nun and I said I wasn't.'

'So you're not upset?'

'Well, I was a bit misquoted. I mean, I never said anything about achieving world peace.'

I can't say the others in the youth group have helped the situation much. Andy has taken to singing 'Climb Every Mountain' when Vanessa enters the room. Julian gave her a tract entitled 'The Scarlet Woman of Babylon – Are You Related?'. Glenda had a blazing row with Vanessa about it.

'I can't believe she's not angry,' she said to me.

'Well,' I said, 'you know what the *Star* is like. It doesn't exactly represent the cutting edge of liberal feminist press.'

'Oh, it's not that,' replied Glenda. 'It's not the fact that it was printed that annoys me. It's the fact that Vanessa has had copies made and is distributing them to her friends. I mean, can't she see what they've turned her into? Despite her crush on you, she's an intelligent woman.'

'Thanks very much.'

'You know what I mean. She's got brains, actually. And she's let herself get turned into a freak. And have you seen what she's taken to wearing? She looks like Britney Spears' mutant cousin.'

She has a point. Ever since the article, Vanessa has taken to wearing rather tight clothes. Well, they're not so much clothes, more wrapping. Yesterday she appeared in church dressed in skin-tight white jeans and a T-shirt with 'Super Vixen' printed on it.

The thing is, I don't know how to react. I've always found the whole issue of 'appropriate clothing' quite confusing, because it seems to me that it's always the girls who get criticised. In the Christian world you never hear of boys causing problems through wearing revealing clothing. (Which is a bit of a relief given the state of the lads in my youth group. I hate to think what unwashed regions are hidden by their grubby attire.)

So part of me feels that it's just plain sexist to be thinking this way. But at the same time, there is no doubt that Vanessa's new fashion sense is causing quite a few of the lads to stumble. (Actually they're more 'falling over themselves' than stumbling.)

So do you have any advice? I've thought about asking Lucy to have a word, but it's a bit difficult asking your girlfriend to talk to another girl because you are having problems with the way she is dressing.

They never told me it was going to be this complicated at Bible College.

Cheers
Chris

From: Chris Francis@Tabernacle.ch.uk
To: Patricia Ryan, P.Ryan@bigplace.com
Subject: Bible study

Pat,

OK. I was lying in bed praying the other night (yes, I do pray, and not just when I'm desperate) and I really felt God say to me that we should get into the Bible a lot more – that we'd let this side of our activities slip.

And I have to admit that God had a point. One of the problems with being in youth ministry is getting the balance right between the activities and the 'Christian' bits. (Yes, yes, I know there's no real distinction, but you know what I mean.) Anyway, I went to see Julie and we discussed the issue.

'I suppose we could make sure that the Sunday night sessions are really Bible studies,' I suggested. 'They seem to have developed into a sort of general hanging-around time.'

'Well, maybe that's what they need,' said Julie. 'I mean, if you've had the Bible chucked at you all day on Sunday, the last thing you need is to have an extra session in the evening.' She looked at me, almost as if she had a confession to make. 'I think,' she said, 'we should start a new group.'

There was a stunned silence.

'Start a new group?' I said. 'Sorry, I must have missed something. Have the government suddenly found an extra 24 hours to shove in every week? Where am I going to find the time?'

'What about Thursdays after school?'

'No, no, I can't do Thursdays,' I said. 'That's the night we have the church meeting, the deacons meeting or the church finance committee.' A light bulb suddenly went on in my head. 'On second thoughts, it's a brilliant idea. And what's more it's a command from God so they can't do anything about it!'

'Well,' said Julie, 'I did say "after school", rather than in the evening.'

'Yes, I know,' I said excitedly, 'but if we plan it right then the meetings will overrun! And I'll never have to go to a deacons meeting again!'

'I'm not entirely sure you're going into this with the right spirit,' said Julie.

So, the next week we had our first planning meeting for the new, after-school Bible studies. It was a younger crowd than usual, with some of the more junior members of the youth group such as Giles, Megan, and Aruna. And, of course, Julian, who, though he claims never to approve of anything I do, still attends virtually every event.

We started by discussing the content.

'Obviously we want to concentrate on justification by faith,' said Julian. 'So I think we should limit the group to the study of Romans.'

'No, no,' said Giles. 'I think we want to look at Psalms. And we shouldn't read them, we should try to sing each one. That way we get the context right.'

'Actually,' said Aruna, 'we don't know if they were all sung, as such. They were probably chanted and in an antiphonal manner. And you would need to play an instrument such as the nablas, or the ten-stringed asor.'

Giles looked blank.

'It's clear,' said Aruna, 'that you don't know your asor from your nablas.'

Various other suggestions were put forward including Lamentations, Song of Songs (twice), the Gnostic Gospel of Thomas and Hezekiah, which sounded interesting, until we realised there isn't a book of Hezekiah.

In the end we decided to postpone the discussion on what we studied to another date.

We went on to style. The air was filled with strident demands.

'I don't want to have endless discussions,' said someone.

'And I don't want to spend ages wading through each chapter in turn,' said another voice.

'And I definitely don't want to have to read anything out loud,' said someone else.

I held my hands up.

'Hold on, hold on,' I said. 'If I understand you right, you want a Bible study, where we don't read it. Or work through it systematically. Or actually discuss it.' I paused. 'This is going to be tricky.'

'But that's the problem, isn't it?' said Giles. 'I mean, I'd like to get into the Bible, but I don't want to do it in the same, boring old way.' There was general assent.

In the end we decided to postpone the discussion on how we did it to another date.

So now I'm stumped. I think they're interested but how do I do Bible study in a way that is going to engage and motivate them? Any ideas?

Cheers
Chris

From: Chris Francis@Tabernacle.ch.uk
To: Patricia Ryan, P.Ryan@bigplace.com
Subject: Independence?

Pat,

I read somewhere once that Liberation Theology was the direct result of leaving poor South American peasants to do their own Bible study. When people read the Bible, they can come up with unexpected conclusions.

I thought about this, this week after starting up the new Bible study group with a look at Ezekiel, concentrating on the prophet's role as a public spokesman for God.

In retrospect, this may have been a mistake.

One of the things we're supposed to be doing, as shepherds and pastors of our flock, is helping them to stand on their own two feet and to walk their own path. This week, the youth group certainly stood on their own two feet, and they didn't so much 'walk their own path' as run away from me in the opposite direction.

Because the day after the Bible study, Megan came to me to discuss her latest 'vision'. Megan has a vision about once a fortnight and, mostly, these are about how much God loves his children and how fluffy he thinks everyone is. But this one was slightly different.

'God is calling us to repent,' she said.

'Absolutely,' I replied. 'He generally does.'

'No, you don't understand. God is calling us to repent – publicly.'

I started to get nervous. 'Er... define "publicly",' I said.

She held her arms out and looked at the ceiling in what, I can only imagine, she thought to be a 'mystical' pose.

'Like Ezekiel,' she declaimed, 'I believe we are being called to show our town an act of public humiliation and repentance on their behalf. I believe that the entire youth group should kneel and pray in the middle of the town as a sign of repentance.' Suddenly she turned and stared at me. 'What do you think?'

'Um... I'll have to think about it,' I said, playing desperately for time. 'I'm not sure it's exactly the best thing to do...'

'Are you denying the validity of my personal revelation?' she inquired.

'Um, no, it's not that,' I said. 'It's just that, well, don't you think that it's a bit over-dramatic? And I'm not sure you really can repent on behalf of others. I rather think they have to do it themselves.'

We then had an hour's discussion on the nature of personal visions, the need for repentance, the symbolic prophecies of Ezekiel and the difficulties of finding a decent place to kneel in public these days. At the end of it I was pretty sure that I'd persuaded Megan that this was not a good idea, and that, basically, we had enough difficulties in the town without the good people of Briglimpton thinking we were all nutters.

So it was with some surprise that I had a phone call two days later from the pastor.

'What's all this about a public act of confession?' he demanded.

'I'm sorry?'

'Well, I've heard you are about to march through the town wearing sackcloth and then pray publicly in front of the town hall. Someone described it as "an act of witness" although witness to what, I'm not sure.'

'I... I... that is... this is nothing to do with me! I was against the idea!'

'Well you'll have to stop it.'

'How can I stop it? They're all free individuals. I can't just order them not to march. I'm their youthworker, not their sergeant major.'

'How could you let this happen?'

'I didn't know they were going ahead. I thought I'd talked Megan out of it.'

'Look, Chris,' he said, 'as a pastor you're supposed to be able to guide people. I'm sure that they mean well. But you can't just let people do whatever they want. It's a question of pastoral techniques.'

After a bit of an investigation I discovered that, far from taking my advice, Megan has gone ahead and organised the whole thing. The youth group will be marching through the town singing hymns and then they will kneel and pray. After that they will give out some tracts that Julian has got hold of, helpfully entitled 'Sodom and Gomorrah – Are They Your Twin Towns?'

I don't know what to do. I've spent the last year and a half hoping they would get off their backsides and witness, and now they've chosen to do it against my advice. I set up evangelistic projects that are modern and relevant and none of them raise a finger. Megan brings back the Middle Ages to Briglimpton and they all join in like a shot.

I'm caught – if I'm right then it will set our evangelism in this town back a few decades. And if Megan is right – then she'll believe that I am no longer to be trusted or listened to. Should I join in? Or go away for the weekend?

Please help!

Cheers
Chris

From: Chris Francis@Tabernacle.ch.uk
To: Patricia Ryan, P.Ryan@bigplace.com
Subject: Mission Impossible

Hi Pat,

The Big Act of Repentance went off OK. In the end I decided I had to support them, so I went along. As it was, it rained so the public march was less of a 'march' and more a 'quick dash from one end of the town to the other'. Apart from Julian, who saw the torrential rain as a chance for suffering in a good cause and deliberately slowed down.

Still, visions are obviously in the air, because the church is embarking on a mission – or, more specifically, on a mission statement. The deacons have been to a seminar on 'A vision for the local church' and have decided that what we need is a church vision. And, as preparation, they have asked each group within the church to come up with their own mission statement.

There is an interesting assortment. The mothers and toddlers group's mission is, apparently, 'To provide high quality care for the under-four's and to kick the butt of the toddler group in the Baptist church'.

The mission statement of the finance sub-committee is 'To increase income, decrease spending and reduce borrowing to less than 2 per cent GDT (Gross Domestic Tithing)'.

Anyway – the time has come to put down my mission statement – to define what we are trying to do through the youthwork in the church.

'Put something vague,' said the pastor. 'That way no one can accuse you of not hitting your goals.'

'Surely the point is to be definite,' I said. 'I mean, your mission statement should be the core of what you are about.'

'Well of course,' said the pastor. 'It's just don't be too detailed. Put down stuff that will be good PR. I put down "To provide relevant, teaching, supportive care and visionary leadership'. However, I didn't add 'to avoid meetings, placate the caretaker and to try to look concerned while the congregation regale me with their petty worries".' He paused.

'You're not having a good week, are you?' I said.

'Don't get me wrong,' he said. 'I think all this is good to do. It's just worthwhile making sure that your mission statement doesn't become an albatross around the neck.'

Anyway, I thought – with my usual naivety – that it would be a good thing to discuss among the youth group themselves. I wondered what they thought we were really here to do. So I gave them a piece of paper with 'The Mission of Youthwork at Briglimpton Tabernacle is...' written at the top.

Here are some sample responses:

Megan: 'To give people lovely moist feelings of warmth, love and mystical awareness and to help them to develop their spiritual auras.'

Glenda: 'To save the planet.'

Andy: 'To have a good time and to get a drinks licence for the tuck shop.'

Vanessa: 'To spread love, to encourage romance.'

Giles: 'To live fast, die young, wear corduroys, bang our heads and praise the Lord.'

Aruna: 'To explore the epistemological and ontological grounds for faith, whilst never neglecting a priori deduction from assumed axioms.'

Julian: 'To convict people of sin, convince them of impending judgement, bring them into the elect and get them to read Calvin's *Institutes*.'

Not hugely helpful then.

So what should be my mission? I know that I want the group to grow in understanding, I know that I want them to stand on their own two feet, I know that I want them to take over the church and change it to what they want and need.

I know I want them to be like Jesus.

Is this enough?

Cheers
Chris

From: Chris Francis@Tabernacle.ch.uk
To: Patricia Ryan, P.Ryan@bigplace.com
Subject: My new apprentice

Hi Pat,

Well, I suppose it's a sign that I am now an experienced youthworker, but now I am being asked to take on an apprentice.

It all started with a phone call on Friday night. The local Baptist church is taking on one of its members as a youthworker – but they want me to act as her mentor.

'We've heard a lot about you,' said the minister. 'But we're still willing to give it a go.'

'Er... thanks very much for that vote of confidence.'

'I've spoken to your pastor and he's agreed.'

'Right.'

'And also to your treasurer and he's agreed.'

'I see.'

'Your church secretary is OK with the idea, as are the rest of the deacons, the worship leader, several members of your youth group and the caretaker.'

By now I was starting to feel annoyed.

'Thank you for bothering to ask me. You seem to have consulted everyone else.'

'Well, we thought it right to be thorough,' he said. 'Can you start immediately?'

'I suppose so.'

'Good.'

The doorbell rang. 'Excuse me,' I said. 'I've got to go, there's someone at the door.'

'I know. That will be her now for her first session.'

'What?'

'Well, you did say you could start immediately,' he said. And hung up.

I opened the door and looked left and right. There was no one there.

'Hello,' said a voice. I looked down and there she was. Four-foot six of denim clad, spiky-haired youthworker. Her nose had so many studs it looked like a jeweller's display case.

'I'm Louise,' she said. 'Your new apprentice.'

She introduced herself. She is twenty-two, single and an HGV driver. She felt called to be a youthworker on a roundabout outside an ASDA store in Leeds.

'It came right out of the blue,' she said. 'I was sitting in my cab having just delivered 14 pallet loads of spuds when I heard the voice of God.'

'When was this?'

'Last Thursday.'

'I see,' I said. 'Good to hear you didn't rush into things.'

'Don't like waiting,' she said. 'Like to get on and do things straight away. Like to be decisive.'

'So you'll be doing this job in your spare time.'

'No,' she said. 'Chucked in my job on Friday morning. Church is going to support me. Had to do a bit of persuading with the minister, but he gave in eventually.'

'Um... what exactly do you mean "gave in"?'

'Well, you know that parable in the Bible about the persistent widow?'

'Yes.'

'Always taken that as a model for action. You'd be amazed how keen he was after the fourteenth phone call.'

'Right,' I said, wondering how to get myself out of this before it was too late. 'That certainly explains his eagerness for me to take you on. But seriously, don't you think that maybe you've rushed things a bit?'

'A call from God is a call from God.' She looked down. 'You probably think I'm being stupid,' she said, 'but I know what I heard God say to me.' She smiled. 'Don't always act this way.'

I thought for a moment.

'OK, I'll give it a go,' I said. 'I guess if it isn't a calling we'll find out soon enough.'

As I talked to her I thought that it was most likely to be a short-term arrangement. Their church has hardly any young people and a dwindling congregation. She will be starting more or less from scratch.

We agreed that Louise is going to 'shadow' me for a month, to see how I do things.

'OK,' I said. 'Do you fancy a coffee?'

'No thanks,' she said, 'but I'll have one of these.' She reached into her bag and brought out a box of herbal teabags. 'Much better for you,' she explained.

'Oh, OK,' I said.

I went into the kitchen, filled the kettle and found two mugs from the debris that passes for the washing up in my flat. When I turned round I nearly had the fright of my life. She was standing right behind me.

'What are you doing?'

'Shadowing you,' she said.

'Listen,' I said, 'you don't have to follow me everywhere and write down everything.'

'Sorry,' she said. 'Just keen.'

'Right. Just take it easy.'

I went to the fridge to get the milk. As I turned round she was right in front of me.

'What kind of milk do you use?' she asked, pencil and notebook in hand.

I think it's going to be a long month.

Cheers
Chris

From: Chris Francis@Tabernacle.ch.uk
To: Patricia Ryan, P.Ryan@bigplace.com
Subject: My new apprentice (2)

Hi Pat,

I told you last email about my new apprentice – Louise the ex-truck driver. She's been shadowing me for a week now – a task which she has approached with a certain amount of zeal. Indeed, it's less like being shadowed and more like being stalked.

At first she was taking notes on everything: how many phone calls I made, how many young people rang the doorbell and when exactly they visited, the contents of my CD shelves and the titles of the books in my bookshelf.

I mean the woman is always scribbling in her notebook. It's like having my own personal government inspector.

Anyway, things came to a head when, once again, she was studying me while I was making a cup of coffee. As I mentioned before, Louise doesn't drink coffee – she brings along a range of herbal teabags, including raspberry and mint; papaya and thyme; and chamomile, mango and cow parsley.

I noticed that she was marking numbers in red in her notebook.

'What are those numbers?' I said, as I handed her a cup of apple and dandelion.

'Your caffeine intake,' she replied, in her usual abrupt style. 'Number of cups of coffee you have during a day. Look, here's a graph.'

She showed me a picture which bore an uncanny resemblance to the skyline of New York.

'Cross-referenced by time of day and by who you've just spoken to on the phone,' she explained. 'See? Your average intake of coffee is 14 cups of day, but that average will rise by 20 per cent if you have had a phone conversation with either your pastor or Julian.'

'14 cups of coffee!' I exclaimed. 'I never have that much.'

'I think you'll find you do.'

'All right, all right,' I said. 'Maybe I do have too much. But it's my way of relaxing.'

'It's very bad for you,' said Louise. 'If you want to relax I know a much better way.'

'Oh, is it one of your herbal remedies?'

She smiled. 'Sort of,' she said. She reached into the pocket of her grubby denim jacket and pulled out a tin, out of which she extracted a chubby, white slug-like object. She held it out to me.

'Here you go,' she said. 'Have a puff of this.'

'Louise!' I said. 'That's a spliff!'

There was a pause. 'Your point is?' she said.

'I don't do drugs!'

'Law's ridiculous about pot.'

'That is not the point. Like it or not, being a youthworker brings responsibilities. It means you don't break the law, you don't set a dangerous example to your youth group.'

'What about your driving?'

'What about it?'

'You break the speed limit.' She gestured to my hi-fi. 'You have copies of your friends' CDs. You're a law-breaker, as well.'

'That is different.'

'Is it? How?'

I wasn't going to let her off the hook.

'Look, Louise,' I said. 'People will look up to you. They will follow your example. Whatever you think about cannabis, you can't afford to put your career in jeopardy by acting in this way. You're going to have to make some sacrifices. You may well be right about the tapes and the driving, but it's different with addictive substances. I don't smoke, and I drink in moderation, because, like it or not, some of my youth group look up to me.'

(At that moment I couldn't exactly think of anyone who did look up to me, but I wasn't about to admit that.)

She shrugged.

'OK,' she said. 'See the point.' She put the pot back in the tin and hid it in the depths of her jacket. 'I'll take it "off-patch",' she said. 'And I'll try to remember about being a role model.'

'Where did you get it?'

'I bought it off one of your youth group,' she said.

So much for role models.

Cheers
Chris

From: Chris Francis@Tabernacle.ch.uk
To: Patricia Ryan, P.Ryan@bigplace.com
Subject: Feedback

Pat,

Louise's presence this month led me to think that maybe I wasn't learning as much as I should be. I thought maybe it was time for me to get some input as well, so I took up the invitation to attend a management seminar the other day.

Ben is a church member, married to Cecily (the elder and church secretary), a local butcher and a leading light in the Briglimpton Chamber of Commerce. He is constantly inviting me to attend what he calls 'Resource Interfaces' but I have resisted so far on the grounds that (a) I'm very busy and (b) all the events are somewhat 'meat' orientated. However, I couldn't hold out forever and on Friday I went to a seminar entitled 'Customer Feedback – Are You "Meating" Their Needs?'

Actually it was quite good, once you got past all the bits about lamb, pork, beef etc. It made me think about how I get feedback from the youth group. And I thought this was the perfect time to get their thoughts on what we should be doing and where we should be going. (Another reason that it's the perfect time is that I haven't got a clue what direction to go in, but I didn't want to let them know that.)

Anyway, I initially invited feedback at the end of a youth group meeting on Sunday night, but all that happened was that Julian started to prophesy against me while everyone else looked bored. In the end the conversation drifted onto other topics such as whether the town's football club was going to win on Saturday and whether Harry Potter was either (a) innately evil or (b) just very irritating. So I devised a simple feedback form and gave it out to all 20 of the Sunday night regulars. I looked forward to some illuminating replies. The results were about as illuminating as a broken torch on a very dark night.

Here are the questions and the summary of the results. Although the form was intended to be anonymous, some of the replies were pretty identifiable:

HOW DO YOU RATE THE YOUTH GROUP?
Better than doing nothing (7)
OK-ish (10)
Quite Good (2)
Excellent (0)
Prone to heresy (1 – Julian)

WHAT KINDS OF ACTIVITIES HAVE YOU ENJOYED MOST?
Sports and games (5)
Discussions (2)
Just Hanging Around (7)
Trips (5)
In-depth Bible studies and prayer for revival (1 – Julian)

WHAT KINDS OF ACTIVITIES WOULD YOU LIKE TO DO IN THE FUTURE?
Don't know (15)
Tango Classes (1 – Vanessa)
Ecological compost-making (1 – Glenda)
Stuffing Julian headfirst into the ecological compost (1 – Andy)
Meditation and Primal Scream Therapy (1 – Megan)
In-depth Bible studies and prayer for revival (1 – Julian)

ARE YOU PREPARED TO TAKE MORE OF A ROLE IN ORGANISING
THESE ACTIVITIES?

Yes (0)

No (20)

WHAT KINDS OF SKILLS AND ABILITIES COULD YOU BRING TO THE
YOUTH GROUP?

None (16)

Passion and patient sacrificial love (1 – Vanessa)

Ecological awareness (1 – Glenda)

Ability to lead in-depth Bible studies and prayer for revival (1 – guess
who)

Desire to stuff the remainder of Julian into the ecologically-made
compost (1 – Andy)

WHAT SUBJECTS SHOULD WE BE DISCUSSING?

Sex (3)

Drugs (5)

Rock and Roll (1 – this came from Giles)

Christianity (1)

Football (5)

Other Faiths (2)

Mysticism (1)

Eco-Terrorism (1)

Predestination (1 – I knew Julian was going to write that)

So all in all a fruitful exercise. I showed the results to Lucy who said,
'What do you expect? It's a stupid way to get their feedback.' However,
she didn't suggest anything better. What do you suggest?

Cheers
Chris

From: Chris Francis@Tabernacle.ch.uk
To: Patricia Ryan, P.Ryan@bigplace.com
Subject: Anxiety

Hi Pat,

It all started with just one question.

As I told you before, Louise has been shadowing me – it's been about a month now. Well, I say "shadowing", it's more like having a bodyguard.

Anyway, it was at the end of one day, just as Louise was about to go when she let drop this little bombshell: 'You think you've been successful as a youthworker?'

I can't remember what I said to her as I closed the door, but once I was alone in the room, I couldn't stop the question bouncing around the walls of my brain.

'Have I been successful?'

In terms of numbers, I suppose it's gone OK. I had visions when I came to the post of becoming the Yonggi Cho of youthwork, of building a youth group roughly the size of a small town. But that hasn't happened. Oh, we've added quite a lot, but I can't help thinking that numbers aren't really the issue.

It worried me so much that I started to make some phone calls.

'Do you think I've been successful?' I asked the pastor.

He paused.

'Oh,' he said, 'you're having one of those moments.'

'What moments?'

'A church-workers' panic attack. Have you been talking to the treasurer? He's not on about introducing productivity-related tithing again, is he?'

'No, I just want to know – do you think I've been successful?'

'You've been fine,' he said, soothingly. 'After all, you're still in the post aren't you?'

It was hardly the most ringing endorsement. But then from his point of view, success is a question of keeping the parents happy. So maybe they were the ones to ask.

'Have I been successful?' I asked Megan's mum.

'Oh,' she said, 'you're having one of those moments.'

'What moments?'

'We all have them. Insecurity. Abandonment. Black despair that gnaws away at the soul.' I began to think that this phone call was not a good idea. 'Terrible, bleak horror of the world,' she continued. Then she paused. 'Still,' she said, 'you've got to laugh haven't you?'

'But have I been successful?'

'Of course you have, dear,' she said. 'You've managed to keep the young people less bored with church than they would be normally. And you keep them out of our hair for large chunks of the week – any parent is always grateful for that.'

Again, I couldn't help that feeling we were working to different definitions of success. I needed a more rigorous, more critical approach.

'Julian,' I said, 'have I been successful?'

'Ah,' he said, 'you're having one of those moments, are you?'

'What moments?' I snarled.

'Moments when God convicts you of the hollowness of worldly success and the need for personal humility before the mercy seat.'

'No I'm not,' I replied. 'I'm just wondering...'

'You are,' he insisted. 'You're having trouble with your mercy seat.'

'Look,' I said, 'forget the pseudo-theology. Just tell me – have I been successful?'

'You're doing your best,' he said. 'I mean the rest of the group seem to like you. I could ask for a more rigorous theological perspective...'

They seem to like me. I'm keeping the young people out of their parents' hair. I haven't been sacked. Was that it?

At bed that night, in the darkness, all the failures kept playing themselves through my mind. All the arguments and the cancellations and the absences and the difficulties and the disappointment.

'God,' I said, 'have I been successful?'

There wasn't an answer.

Then, I seemed to hear a voice.

'Ah,' said God. 'You're having one of those moments, are you?'

And then, instead of the bad things, I began to think of the good things. I began to think of events that had worked, of times when the young people had shown their walk with God in action, of new converts, of friendship and laughter. And Julian's words seem to echo in my mind: 'You're doing your best'.

Numbers weren't the issue. Activities were not that important. If the young people were growing in their walk with God, then that was all that mattered.

I'm not the greatest youthworker in the world. Revival has not broken out in the town. I haven't become a youthwork guru. I'm just working hard, seeing small victories, and trying to keep close to God.

Maybe that's about as successful as any of us ever get.

Cheers
Chris

From: Chris Francis@Tabernacle.ch.uk
To: Patricia Ryan, P.Ryan@bigplace.com

Subject: Music

Hi Pat,

Giles is a good lad, committed Christian and all that. He plays in the worship band. But his taste in music has always tended towards the 'heavy'. I never really worried about this, except when trying to tell him not to put so much distortion on the guitar when he's leading worship.

But recently I wondered if his tastes hadn't got a bit too extreme. I only realised this when, taking him up on his suggestion, I organised an evening of discussing their favourite music with the youth group. People brought along stuff to play and we had a pretty fruitful discussion ranging from homophobia in rap music and whether it was any different to the church's homophobia, to the age-old question of whether the representation of sex and relationships in modern music is fulfilling and positive.

And then Giles put his CD on. Now, Giles doesn't exactly look like a hard-core rocker. He stands just over five foot in his socks and has curly blond hair and glasses. He wears heavy metal T-shirts, it is true, but tends to combine them with corduroy trousers and a pair of Hush Puppies. However he has hidden depths. Some quite alarming hidden depths.

'This is heavy metal, is it?' I asked.

'I'm more into death metal myself,' he began. 'Although I do like quite a lot of thrash, grind and doom.'

'You've obviously heard Julian preach,' said Andy.

Julian looked at him. 'I am closing my ears to this whole discussion,' he said.

(It hadn't been an easy night for Julian, who still regards Gregorian chant as inherently sinful.)

'But my favourite band are this lot,' continued Giles. He held up a CD which appeared to show a bare-chested Viking drinking something from a skull.

'I've been to pubs like that,' said Glenda.

'They're called Filthscum,' said Giles. 'And the track is called "Hello".'

At least that's what I thought he said. But it turned out the track was called 'Hell-Oh'. If I'd realised, perhaps I'd have stepped in sooner.

It started with huge, grinding chords and then the lead vocalist started screaming. I call him lead vocalist, but that's only because he was, presumably, using his vocal chords. You couldn't call it singing, or even shouting. It was more like someone in pain.

The lyrics began:

I've chosen the dark, I've chosen the night
I've turned out the lamp, I've switched off the light.
I'm going into the bottomless pit
On my leather trousers I sit.

(More screaming)

'I think his leather trousers might be a bit too tight,' said Andy.

So far, so funny. But then the second verse began to worry me.

The fiends of hell are friends of mine,
I'm feeling good, I'm feeling fine.
The emptiness annihilates all…

Chorus: More screaming followed by the word 'disembowel' chanted 14 times.

'This is where it gets good,' said Giles.

And this is where I stop writing the lyrics. Because after that the song consisted of a description of someone being tortured and a hymn of praise to someone who was called 'The unholy lord of the earth'. After it came to an end, Giles looked round the room and blinked innocently. There was a deep silence. Even Andy looked shocked. No one said anything.

'Thank you, Giles,' I said. 'Umm, that was very...' He looked at me. I ran out of words.

'Did you like it?' he asked.

'Giles,' I said. 'The lyrics... have you actually thought about what you're listening to?'

'They're just lyrics,' he said. 'It's just a pose. They don't really mean it.'

'No, Giles, this is not Eurovision. This is not someone writing la-la-la just to fill out the tune. This is nihilism and despair and... and worse.'

He looked crushed.

'I think you're being unfair. After all some of the stuff you listen to isn't so pure.'

'You're right. But there's a difference between that and something that is just so... so evil.'

'Oh yes?' he said. 'And what's the difference then? What difference is there between one unchristian lyric and another?'

Well, we got into a discussion, and some took Giles' side and more took mine and I must admit I wasn't really sure how to answer him. But I felt that this music was on a different level. Pop music might be immoral, but this was blasphemous.

In the end I suggested that I would drop in on Giles later this week and listen to some more stuff and talk about it. I don't know if this is the right thing to do, but I couldn't think of any other way to tackle it. After everyone had gone home, Julian was left sitting there.

'Go on,' I said.

'What?'

'Tell me I should have condemned him or burnt him at the stake. Or give me a tract about it.'

He looked at me. 'No, I was thinking about that statement. About how it was all just a pose. And I was thinking that, well, a lot of things start off in life as a pose, don't they? People start pretending to be something and then, the pretending bit takes over. It's like the pose becomes the person. The style becomes the substance. And everything really is darkness.'

I looked at him. And then I said something I never thought I'd hear myself saying.

'Julian,' I said. 'Shall we pray?'

Cheers
Chris

From: Chris Francis@Tabernacle.ch.uk
To: Patricia Ryan, P.Ryan@bigplace.com
Subject: The Annual General Meeting

Hi Pat,

You wanted to know how my presentation at the church's Annual General Meeting went. Here's a rough idea.

THE SCENE: Briglimpton Tabernacle Church Hall. Out the front is a table, at which the PASTOR sits with the air of one who has given up caring. He looks like the writer of Ecclesiastes must have looked at that moment when he realised how futile everything was. Next to him sits the CHURCH SECRETARY. On the other side is the TREASURER. He sits back in his chair, arms folded across his chest, his entire demeanour proclaiming 'they're not going to get anything out of me'.

CHRIS THE YOUTHWORKER is sitting on the front row. He has a sheaf of papers, some acetates. Behind him sit the CHURCH MEMBERS. Most of these are over eighty – not that the church is full of eighty-year-olds, it's just that those who are younger have better things to do than attend church business meetings.

PASTOR: And now we come to item 47 on the agenda – youthwork. I have asked Chris to give a brief presentation about the youthwork in the church. Just to keep you up to date. So – over to Chris.

CHRIS: Thanks very much. Well it's really great to have this opportunity to talk to you about youthwork...

SECRETARY: (Snorts)

CHRIS: And to share with you a little of where I think we're going and what our needs will be.

TREASURER: (Snorts)

CHRIS: I've bought a few acetates to show you some of what we get up to...

STANLEY THE CARETAKER: It's broken.

CHRIS: Sorry?

STANLEY: The Overtop Projectile thingy. It's broken. Someone sat on it.

PASTOR: They sat on it?

STANLEY: (He stares at the youthworker) One of the young people thought it were a photocopier and tried to make a photocopy of their...

CHRIS: (Interrupting) Yes, well, I'll make sure they pay for it. Well, let's forget about the acetates. I'll just have to explain myself.

There follows a lengthy explanation of the youthwork in the church, touching on strategic planning, group dynamics, relevant theories of youth and adolescent development, global warming, the state of the world economy, the price of fuel and many other important issues.

PASTOR: (Waking up) Yes, thank you for all that. Now are there any questions?

CHURCH MEMBER: How many?

CHRIS: Er... how many what?

CHURCH MEMBER: How many have you converted?

CHRIS: Well, that's a difficult question to answer...

CHURCH MEMBER: No it's not. My father was a missionary in the Sudan and he always knew how many he'd converted. He kept notes.

CHRIS: Yes, well, young people today live in a very different world. However, it is true to say that we have seen some make commitments and we have made contact with loads more – especially through working in schools and open youth groups...

CHURCH MEMBER: Yes, but have you ministered the gospel? My father always said that our only job was to minister the gospel. He was a missionary in the Sudan, you know.

CHRIS: You said. It depends what you...

CHURCH MEMBER: Have they been washed in the blood of the Lamb?

CHRIS: I don't think many of them have been washed in anything. Not recently anyway.

CHURCH MEMBER: My father always knew how many were washed in the blood of the Lamb. He went out to the Sudan, you know.

CHRIS: Have you thought about following his example?

PASTOR: I think what Chris is trying to say is that his world is a little bit different to your father's, Harry.

CHRIS: It's wetter for a start.

CHURCH MEMBER: Aye. But he needs to remember what he's here for. We don't pay him to make relationships. We pay him to make converts.

CHRIS: With respect, I don't think you can make one without the other. Most of the young people we meet have no idea what the church is, what it believes, or why they should be interested. I want to do more work with those kinds of kids. That's why I think this church needs to have a greater vision for the youthwork.

SECRETARY: (Snorts)

CHRIS: (Ignoring her) We need to pour our time, energy and money into it...

TREASURER: (Snorts)

CHRIS: I have a chart here showing the figures. Do you realise how many young people are leaving the church every week?

CHURCH MEMBERS: (Snore)

PASTOR: Well, I'd like to thank Chris for that helpful presentation. (Quietly to CHRIS) I think that went very well, don't you?

Well, that was what it felt like anyway. I'm not worried – the support I get from the rest of the church is really great. But sometimes, I must admit, even my most ardent supporters have that question at the back of their minds: 'How many has he converted?'

And their fathers weren't even in the Sudan.

Cheers

Chris

From: Chris Francis@Tabernacle.ch.uk
To: Patricia Ryan, P.Ryan@bigplace.com
Subject: New staff

Hi Pat,

Well, Andy has decided to call it a day. He's setting up his own mechanics business and he says that he needs to take a break.

So we need to replace a member of the team. Not exactly an unusual occurrence, but Andy was such a stalwart that it's made the process a bit more daunting. Normally I just approach suitable candidates and use a cunning mixture of flattery, emotional blackmail and plain begging until they give in. One of my team said that she was not so much called into youthwork as nagged into it.

However, this time I thought I'd look for some fresh blood. So I put a notice in the notice sheet, asking anyone who was interested to see me after the service. Nobody spoke to me. I don't mean 'nobody spoke to me about the youthwork', nobody spoke to me at all. I think they were scared that, if they opened up the most innocent conversation with me I would mesmerise them with my special youthworker stare until they would lose all will of their own.

So, the next week I thought I'd go for a more direct approach, and I stood up and explained the need. I was impassioned. I was informed. I was ignored. It was like being engulfed in a tidal wave of apathy. Never have I seen so many people suddenly pretend to read their Bibles.

Of course, no one responded. I moaned about it at our team meeting the next day.

'If getting volunteers was easy,' said the pastor, 'we wouldn't have to employ youthworkers.'

'Nonsense!' I retorted. 'Youthworkers are skilled, trained professionals.'

'So are stunt men,' replied the pastor. 'Still doesn't mean that everyone wants to have a go. I think you ought to try a different approach.'

'What do you mean?'

'Just stop lecturing people.'

'I have never lectured people!'

He sighed. 'Your appeal on Sunday included a three minute-sermon on the ethics of servanthood. I thought you were going to ask the organist to play a hymn while people came to the front.'

'All right, I might have lectured a bit.'

'Just try explaining,' he suggested. 'Let people understand the need and see what God wants them to do.'

So, the following Sunday I took a different approach. I put up a display about our work, and simply stood and answered questions afterwards. I had some of the youth group with me to explain the kinds of things we did. I still haven't replaced Andy – but on the other hand some people have shown real interest. All I need do now is follow them up with phone calls every half hour until their resolve weakens.

Mind you, all of this change has got me thinking about my future here; about how much longer I will stay – and even whether I should be changing jobs. I guess this was thrown into further relief by a chance meeting I had with an old friend of mine.

Ian is a youthworker. He's been a youthworker now for around fifteen years. But when we bumped into each other the other day in the pub he didn't seem very keen on youthwork.

'I've been thinking about moving on,' he said. 'But it's really difficult. I mean, what else would I do?'

'What do you mean – there must be loads of stuff you could do.'

'Like what?'

'Er... I don't know,' I said. 'Loads of stuff.'

'You see?' he said triumphantly. 'Youthwork is a great job – but what does it train you to do? Where's the career progression?'

'I don't know if I've ever thought about it,' I said. 'I guess I didn't come into youthwork for a "career". Come to think of it, I've never made a career move in my life.'

'But that's the point,' he said. 'Youthwork – particularly church-based youthwork – is a young profession. It's just starting to grow up. And now you're getting people who have been doing it for some time and are wondering what to do next.'

'People like you.'

'Exactly. I'm stuck. I don't know where to go to from here.'

'Well, you could go to the bar for one thing,' I suggested, offering him my glass. I looked at him for a moment. 'Do you still enjoy it?' I said. 'Do you still get the buzz?'

He shrugged his shoulders and stared down at his drink.

'When I started, it was a cause,' he said. 'It was all I wanted to do, all I wanted to be. I had loads of ideas, loads of energy.'

'And now?'

'Now...' he paused. 'Now it's just a job.'

I must admit the conversation shook me a little. Not because of Ian's depression – he's always been like that. No, the reason I took notice was because I've seen the same thing in so many Christian leaders, teachers, youthworkers. The people who started out full of zeal and have settled down into quiet efficiency. I've seen preachers who started out wanting to change the world get to the point where all they want to do is change jobs.

And maybe that's the way it has to be. In some ways I don't see why youthwork – or any kind of ministry – should be that different from doing any other job. You start out with energy and drive and then a cause turns into a career.

I also see the same thing happening among churches. I mean, compare a new convert with someone who has been a Christian for 20 years. Which one has the more excitement, the more energy? I'd hazard a guess that in most cases it's the new Christian.

So maybe it's just human nature. Maybe it's just the way we're wired. Start out at a sprint and slow down into a gentle jog.

And don't get me wrong – I'm still enjoying what I'm doing. It all happens efficiently. It's all going very well.

So I should be content. Except that part of me doesn't want it to be that way. I want to feel passionate about youthwork again. I want to feel excited, thrilled, challenged, irritated, angry, exasperated... My youthwork has turned into a merry-go-round, when it started out as a rollercoaster.

So how do I get the old flame back? Or is it really time for a new challenge and a new career?

Cheers
Chris

From: Chris Francis@Tabernacle.ch.uk

To: Patricia Ryan, P.Ryan@bigplace.com

Subject: **The Big Day**

Pat,

Sorry I haven't spoken to you for a while but it's been a bit hectic here.

Life over Christmas was the usual mad rush. During these weeks, the pastor turns into a snarling monster. He has so many carol services to do – the local school, the old people's club – he gets heartily sick of the whole affair.

Anyway, I decided to get the youth group involved and we helped out with the nativity play for the Sunday school to perform in church. Julian wrote the script which was quite good (although I did have to cut a long speech by the angel Gabriel on predestination) and Vanessa directed it. She's very good with kids, largely because she is so childish herself. (I think she has got over the shock of me being with another woman, although she did ask me the other day if Christians were definitely not allowed to use voodoo dolls.) Glenda, who by this stage was in an advanced state of pregnancy, was doing the prompt. She was very fed up with things, and was not helped when Giles looked at her and suggested that instead of doing the Christmas story we should be doing Jonah and the Whale.

Anyway, the play went swimmingly. Young Jonathan Fleming played Joseph with the aid of a stick-on beard and a tea towel wrapped round his head and the three kings rather changed the course of history by presenting the baby Jesus with some bubble bath, a pair of Tellytubby pyjamas and a PlayStation. Because of the argument between the Taylor twins over which of them should play Mary, in the end they both did. Rebecca did one scene, and Roberta the next, and the audience never noticed, until the final scene when they both appeared together. Several of the congregation thought they had suddenly developed double vision.

It was just as things were coming to their climax and the angel Gabriel was saying 'Thus it is that we are elected and pre-ordained to Glory...' when Glenda gestured to me.

'Quick!' she hissed. 'Something terrible is happening!'

I looked up to the stage. 'It's only the children singing "Away in a Manger",' I said. 'It's not exactly in tune, but even so...'

'Not up there!' she snarled, pointing to her stomach. 'Down there!' She grabbed hold of my hand with a grip like a bulldog's jaws. 'The baby's coming!'

As 'Away in a Manger' ended, I stood up.

'Is there a doctor in the house?' I asked.

Glenda's grip on my hand was now excruciatingly painful.

Fortunately we are replete with medical staff in our church and several GPs, three nurses, two radiologists and a hospital porter came forward. They found some screens and put them round.

By now I had lost all feeling in my hand. Vanessa was on the other side of Glenda. 'Be brave,' she said.

'I'm trying,' I replied through gritted teeth.

'Not you, her!' snapped Vanessa.

'Don't leave me!' said Glenda.

'We won't,' said Vanessa.

'I can't,' I said.

Someone phoned an ambulance, but it was evident from Glenda's yells that it was all happening rather fast.

'Don't worry,' said one of the many health-care professionals at the other end of Glenda. 'You're in perfectly safe hands. Just take deep breaths.'

I took several. It certainly helped.

'Where's my mum?' asked Glenda.

'Your parents are on their way,' I said, knowing full well that as they had been tracked down on a shopping trip several miles away, it would take some time.

'I can't do it without them,' said Glenda.

'Yes you can,' said Vanessa. 'We're your family. We're all here for you.'

By the time the ambulance men arrived it was decided that she was better where she was. A few moments later there was a loud yell from Glenda, a cheer from the church members at the other end and a scream of 'You've done it!' from Vanessa. And there, wrapped in swaddling bands (well, Jonathan Fleming's tea cloth actually) was a little baby boy.

Glenda finally released my hand. It had turned a nasty bluish colour. She held the little boy close to her. 'Hello,' she said. 'You certainly knew how to make an entrance, didn't you?' After a while the youth group gathered round.

'What will you call him?' asked Julian.

'I'm going to name him after one of my heroes,' said Glenda. 'I'm going to call him Calvin.'

'That's beautiful,' Julian whispered. 'What a fine tribute to a great Protestant leader.'

'Oh,' said Glenda. 'I didn't know he was a Protestant. But I've always liked his underwear.'

Cheers
Chris

From: Chris Francis@Tabernacle.ch.uk

To: Patricia Ryan, P.Ryan@bigplace.com

Subject: Welcome Calvin

Hi Pat,

I've just got back from one of the weirdest events of my life: the dedication for Glenda's baby. Originally it was planned to be as part of the morning service, but when the pastor saw what was planned he felt it was better to 'give it the space it needed' in a more prominent time, i.e. 3:00 on Friday afternoon.

Anyway, I can't really describe the event itself, here's what was on the printed running order. (As most of the hymns and songs were new to me, I've typed them in as well.)

Dedication and Thanksgiving

for the Birth of

CALVIN GAIA EL NINO HOGARTH

Welcome from Pastor George Richards

Hymn 373 'Celestial Orbs'

Celestial Orbs with splendour throb
In firmament on high,
All nature cries: 'You've got the job,
Great Patron of the Skies.'

You made the mountains very high
Their height by you was set,
The deserts, they are really dry
And the seas are really wet.

So Lord receive our praises
For flowers that grow in spring
For buttercups and daisies
And every blooming thing.

Reading: Psalm 19

After which GLENDA (mother) and MEGAN (friend) will lead the congregation in symbolic movements based on fertility rituals of the Hopi tribe.

Song 67 'Heal our Land, Lord'

(Men) Heal our Land, Lord
(Women) Land Lord, land Lord.
(Men) Make it good, Lord
(Women) Good Lord, good Lord.
(Men) In your time, Lord
(Women) Time Lord, time Lord.
(Men) In your hands Lord
(Women) Hands Lord, hands Lord.
(Men) It's a crime, Lord
(Women) Crime Lord, crime Lord.
(Men) All creation pants, Lord
(Women) Pants Lord, pants Lord.

(Repeat until sick of it)

Act of Thanksgiving led by our youthworker, Chris Francis

Prayers: Julian Carey

(Coffee and light refreshments will be served while Julian is praying)

Final Prayers

Anyway, you get the idea. The music was led by Giles who did it quite well, although I think the heavy fuzz bass during the hymn was a bit unnecessary – especially since it woke the baby up. The symbolic movements were interesting although I didn't see them all since I was having a symbolic movement of my own.

My bit was... nerve-wracking. I'd worked really hard on what I was going to say. As you know I'm not a natural speaker and I wanted it to be just right. So I spoke about Jesus and children and about what his own childhood must have been like. I suppose I just wanted to let little Calvin know that his mum loved him and we loved him and God loved him.

I thought it went OK. Everyone seemed happy. Except for Glenda's parents who sat tight-lipped throughout the whole thing. Afterwards they came up to me.

'I hope you enjoyed it,' I said.

'Hardly the word I'd use, really,' said her mother. 'We got through it.'

'And next time you do one of these,' said her father, 'you might think about putting something biblical in there.'

'Er... I thought I was quite biblical,' I stammered.

'You didn't mention sin,' said her mother. 'Not once.'

'Perhaps,' said her father, 'if you'd mentioned it more during your times with the young people we wouldn't be in this position, eh?'

I paused.

'I'll tell you what,' I said. 'We'll split the responsibilities. You carry on telling everyone – Glenda, me, little Calvin – what sinners we are. I'll carry on telling them that God loves them. That way we can both be happy.'

They didn't answer. Just stormed out. I shouldn't have said it, I know, but they make me so angry.

Part of it was because I'd worked so hard on that dedication, I so wanted what I said to be, well, healing, I suppose. But if I'm honest part of me is worried by what they say. Maybe they're right. Maybe I didn't teach Glenda well enough.

Could I have done anything different? I don't know.

Cheers
Chris

From: Chris Francis@Tabernacle.ch.uk
To: Patricia Ryan, P.Ryan@bigplace.com

Subject: Ministries v. jobs

Hi Pat,

As you know Lucy and I are due to get married in a few months' time – an event which many of the church members are seeing as their major social occasion of the year. Of course, the real problem is knowing who to invite – or, rather, who not to invite. The negotiations over invitations and seating plans have been like arranging a diplomatic treaty. We're going to have to get the UN in to keep the peace.

The church is very much looking forward to having a married youthworker – mainly because they think that Lucy will automatically become my deputy, an attitude that is starting to cause her serious irritation. We were talking to Cecily – the church secretary – the other day and I was mentioning the problems we're having staffing the Tuesday night youth group.

'Well, you'll soon have some extra help, won't you?' Cecily said.

'Will I?' I replied hoping for a moment that Cecily was going to volunteer.

'Of course,' she replied. 'When you're married.'

There was a pause. Lucy smiled at her. I shivered. The last time I saw a smile like that it was on the face of a crocodile who had just spotted lunch.

'I see,' she said. 'So I'm marrying into youthwork, am I?'

'Well, I just thought that you'd want to get involved.'

'How many days do you spend at your husband's work?' asked Lucy. 'I mean, when you get home from the office, do you rush out to join your husband at the butcher's counter?'

'He is not a butcher,' replied the church secretary, rather haughtily. 'He is a meat production executive.'

'Oh, come on Cecily,' I said. 'He makes sausages.' There was a long pause. 'Very good ones,' I added, rather lamely.

'Anyway, the point we're trying to make,' said Lucy, rather hurriedly, 'is that you wouldn't be expected to be an unpaid helper at his work, would you? So...'

Cecily looked at us both.

'It's not the same thing at all,' she said. 'Ben has a job.' She pointed to me. 'You have a ministry.'

I don't think Lucy was hugely impressed by this distinction. She will, and indeed does, help out with the youth group. But I think if she feels it is sort of expected of her, she might not be so willing. It's one thing to be a volunteer, quite another thing to be an unpaid helper.

And a few days later I had my own problems with the idea of 'ministry', when Lucy and I had a meeting with a bloke about arranging a mortgage. He took down the details of Lucy's salary and then looked at mine.

'So,' he said, looking at the figures I'd scribbled down, 'what else do you do?'

'Er... nothing,' I said. 'I mean, I look at the television, play a bit of squash. Go out to the movies quite a lot.'

'No,' he said. 'What other job do you have? Where do you get the rest of your income from?'

I shook my head. 'That's all I get. I'm a church-based youthworker. That's my pay.'

He stared at me.

'This isn't a wage,' he said. 'This is a generous tip.'

He began to explain the position in detail, but the truth is, I've never been very good with figures. When anyone mentions the word 'budget', my eyes glaze over and I start to lose consciousness. What was apparent, though, was that my salary was on the insignificant side of paltry and that, as long as that was the case, Lucy and I could look forward to starting married life together in a small shoe box.

Suddenly came the understanding that I didn't want to give up youthwork, but neither did I want to carry on living on a pittance. How could I afford to get married and still continue doing what I love? I realised why so many of my contemporaries give up full-time youthwork; it's not that they've fallen out of love with youthwork, it's just that they can't afford it any more. So they move on, take on supposedly more 'serious' roles. With a sinking heart, I realised that I may have to follow them, that it might be time, to use a term that my mother is fond of employing, for me to 'get a proper job'.

We stood outside the mortgage office and looked at each other.

'I'm sorry,' I said to Lucy. 'I never realised... I mean, I know it doesn't pay very well. Not like your job.'

She sighed.

'That's the problem,' she said. 'It's not a job. It's a ministry.'

Cheers
Chris

From: Chris Francis@Tabernacle.ch.uk
To: Patricia Ryan, P.Ryan@bigplace.com
Subject: Ah romance...

Hi Pat,

I thought it was a good idea. A Valentine's Day party; we've done one before and it worked really well. But when I suggested it to Megan she gave me one of those looks. You know, the kind of look that only takes a moment, but which manages to say, 'You are an unfeeling, uncaring male with all the sensitivity and understanding of a fence post.' Obviously there was much more going on in my youth group than I knew about.

'I think that would be a bit of a problem,' said Megan.

'Oh, who's broken up with who, now?' I asked.

Then the whole story came out.

'Luke has chucked Donna,' said Megan.

'Oh,' I said, trying to disguise the fact that I didn't even know they were together. 'That's a shame.'

'No, that's not the shame,' said Megan. 'That's OK, because Donna wants to go out with Richard.'

'Oh.'

'But Richard was going out with Kathryn. So they've split up.'

'I see. That's the problem.'

I tried to look understanding and sensitive, but Megan gave me another withering look. 'No, that's not the problem. Kathryn didn't really want to go out with Richard anyway. She was only doing it because she really wants to go out with his brother.'

There was a pause. 'Er... isn't Richard's brother only seven?'

She sighed. 'His other brother,' she said. 'Darren. You know, he works in the butcher's shop.'

I thought for a moment. 'Darren!' I said. 'Do you mean Neanderthal Norrington? You can't be serious. He has a tattoo on his forehead.'

She looked at me. 'You shouldn't judge by appearances,' she said.

'No, I know. But let's face it, with Darren there isn't much else to judge by. He's only just managed to walk upright. I mean, the creature is still evolving.' I tried to picture him and Kathryn together and gave up. It would be like the Queen going out with Ozzy Osbourne. 'I just didn't think he was Kathryn's type,' I said.

'He isn't,' she said.

Suddenly the fog lifted. 'Ah,' I said. 'So that's the problem.'

She snorted. 'Don't you listen to anything? That's not the problem.'

The fog descended again. 'Oh. But you just said he wasn't her type.'

'Which is exactly why she wants to go out with him,' she said. She laughed. 'Don't you know anything about women?'

'I thought I did,' I said. 'Before this conversation started.'

'Anyway,' Megan continued. 'Kathryn is going out with Justin instead, just, you know, marking time. And of course, Justin has chucked Ruth.'

There was a long pause.

'And... er... is that the problem?' I inquired.

'Of course not. Ruth's going out with Luke.'

'I see.' There was an even longer pause. 'Remind me again who Luke was going out with?'

She took a deep breath. 'Luke was with Donna, but he chucked her to go out with Ruth who was chucked by Justin so that he could go out with Kathryn, only Kathryn wants to go out with Darren, which is why she split up from Richard and now Richard's going out with Donna who has just been chucked by Luke.' She looked at me. She waved her hand in front of my now fully glazed-over eyes. 'Shall I draw you a diagram?'

I shook my head. 'But if everyone's going out with someone else and they all seem fairly happy about it,' I asked, 'then what's the problem with holding a Valentine's party?'

'The problem,' she said, 'is that I haven't got a thing to wear.'

This conversation has brought to mind a whole area of the youth group that I have always felt slightly out of my depth in. It seems to me that one of the key things we can be doing in Christian or church-based groups is to give young people a safe environment in which to make – and even break – relationships. That's part of growing up. (Or evolving in Darren's case.)

But it's a difficult thing to keep tabs on. Part of this, I admit, is because Megan was right: I do have the sensitivity of a fence post. I wouldn't want to classify it as a male thing, but it's true. So I rely on others to let me know what's happening. The problem is that others often keep me in the dark.

So, given all these complications, how do I approach the issue? What kinds of teaching should I be giving them on relationships? What help is there for a fence post in this most convoluted area of youthwork?

Cheers
Chris

From: Chris Francis@Tabernacle.ch.uk
To: Patricia Ryan, P.Ryan@bigplace.com
Subject: Darren the disciple

Hi Pat,

Something really good has come out of last month's Valentine's Day party. I made a point of getting to know some of the fringe members of the youth group a bit better.

As a result of which I had a phone call from Kathryn. Kathryn lives on one of the really posh, private estates that run back from the seafront west of the town and up till now she's only been interested in horses and ponies. I can only remember her contributing to a Bible study once and that was to inquire what kind of horses were pulling Jehu's chariot. A question I found myself completely unable to answer. (I must have missed the 'Equine Identification in the Time of Kings' lecture at college.) I tried to sidestep the question by claiming that he was actually harnessed to a very fast camel, but she wasn't convinced.

Recently, however, she's been a lot more interested in Christianity. She's even started helping out in the Sunday school (although I think that may have something to do with getting out of the pastor's sermons). Anyway she talked about her faith and how difficult it was for her to talk to her friends about it. So I gave her some books, which I thought she might find helpful.

Obviously they were helpful. Because two days ago, she phoned me.

'I've been speaking to a friend of mine about Christianity,' she said, excitedly.

'Brilliant.'

'And now he wants to talk to you.'

'Right.' I paused. 'Er... why does he want to talk to me?'

'Well, he's got some questions and I thought you'd be better at answering them.'

I paused again. 'This isn't anything about horses, is it?' I inquired.

'No! It's about Christianity. He just needs to talk to someone more at his level.'

'Oh, I see,' I said, smugly. Obviously her friend was an intellectual who needed to really grapple with the deep theological issues. 'Who is this exactly?'

'Darren Norrington.'

The image of deep and intellectually stimulating debate disappeared like a puff of smoke. I'd met Darren plenty of times. In fact, he was the kid on the church steps puffing a cigarette, the one who inspired me to set up the Tuesday night group. He never did come to that much, but

I've always tried to chat with him whenever I've seen him. The last time was a few days ago in the butcher's shop where he is now serving as an apprentice. This is a boy who routinely cuts up and sells creatures more intelligent than he is. Darren's idea of an intellectual challenge is working out how to put his trousers on.

Still, I agreed to meet with him, and, that night, he came round.

'So Darren,' I said. 'What do you want to know?'

'Well,' he said, 'Kath's been talking to me, right. 'Bout church and all that.'

There was a pause.

'Right,' I said.

'And I bin thinking.'

There was another pause.

'Right,' I said again.

'What I want to know is: why?' he said.

'Er... do you mean, why has Kathryn been talking to you?'

'No. I mean, why does it all matter? Why did Jesus die? Why does God care about us? If there is a God, why can't we see him? Why doesn't he talk to us? If all this is true, why isn't church more exciting? And why do all you lot act so superior?'

As it all poured out of him, suddenly I felt very ashamed. 'Don't judge others and you won't be judged,' said Jesus and we always give this a very spiritual spin. But maybe he just meant that we shouldn't take people at their face value. We shouldn't judge by appearances. Which is exactly what I'd done with Darren.

One of the things we do in youthwork is confuse depth of feeling with linguistic ability. We think that people can't have profound questions, profound feelings, profound thoughts unless they have passed their exams. And in church we get so used to dealing with the well-educated middle-class that we can no longer communicate with the rest of our society.

All this went through my brain as I struggled to answer his questions. We had a great time together, but it was difficult. It's not made any easier because most of the resources we produce are aimed at people who can read. And reading isn't Darren's strength.

But he could think. And he could question. And he could understand that God loves him. And – praise the Lord – he could respond to that love and make a commitment.

I've seldom felt so excited at anyone coming to Christ. But now I have to disciple him. And what materials can I use to disciple somebody like Darren? I can't give him the type of material I gave Kathryn. He's not going to read his Bible, he's going to find the church service remote and uninteresting and confusing.

So how do we disciple those kids who come from different educational backgrounds? In a religion that is based so much around a book, how do we disciple people who can't – or don't – read?

Cheers
Chris

From: Chris Francis@Tabernacle.ch.uk
To: Patricia Ryan, P.Ryan@bigplace.com
Subject: Story-time

Hi Pat,

It's going well with Darren. You know, it's easy to get caught up in the paraphernalia of youthwork; to get immersed in theory and resources and structures and events and all that. But I'd forgotten just how thrilling it is to see someone start a relationship with God for the first time and to see that relationship develop and grow.

However, the whole thing has got me thinking about the way we communicate with young people and whether our teaching is really working. I rang up a mate of mine who is training to be a missionary. He's joined an organisation called 'Mission Objective Of Converting Our World'. (Not only does this seem a rather ambitious aim, but the initials spell MOOCOW.)

Anyway, I asked him what the best way of communicating was in a non-book culture.

'Use a narrative-driven, intriguing, sequential-event scenario,' he said.

'Eh?'

'Tell them a story.'

'I don't know any stories,' I said. 'And anyway, I'm rubbish at that sort of thing. You know me. I can't even tell a knock-knock joke without getting confused.'

He sighed. Perhaps he was regretting answering the phone to this idiot, when he could have been out changing the world.

'Of course you know some stories. And if you don't, ask others. Everyone has a story to tell. I promise you that when you start swapping stories, things happen.'

Now that intrigued me. So, the next time the youth group were together we started to talk about stories and I asked them what stories they would tell a non-Christian to inspire or move them.

'I'd tell them the story of the rich fool,' said Julian. 'About how he thought he had everything but really he was doomed and going to hell. And then I'd point out to my listeners that even though they aren't rich, they are still doomed and going to hell.'

There was a thoughtful silence.

'And you find that encouraging, do you?' said Aruna.

'Well, what would you tell them?' asked Julian.

'I'd tell them the story of the ark of the covenant, describing in detail the ephod along with some theories as to how exactly the ancient Israelites were able to stand the ephod up and discoursing on the possibility that there were several "arks" as discussed in the theories of Grierson and Munro-Hay.'

There was an even longer silence.

'Well, that would have them rolling in the aisles!' said Kathryn.

'All right, what would you suggest?'

Kathryn thought for a moment.

'How about *Black Beauty*?'

'Er... is that in the Bible?'

'Not exactly,' said Kathryn. 'But it's my favourite book.'

'Don't know which is my favourite book,' said Giles. 'It's either *The Lord of the Rings* or *The Matt Redman Song Book*.'

'I like *The Vegan's Guide to Civilian Disobedience*,' said Glenda.

'I've got a lovely book of Ignatian meditations,' said Megan. 'It's either that or my Taizé Liturgy book.'

'If you ask me,' said Julian, 'you can't beat Calvin's *Institutes*. Why they haven't made a film of it yet beats me.'

'Look,' I interrupted, 'we were supposed to be coming up with meaningful stories, not discussing our favourite literature.'

They thought for a moment.

'I know what we ought to do,' said Julian. 'We should simply tell them the story about Jesus, but do so in a way they would listen.' There was general agreement, and Julian sat back looking as though he had just come up with the most revolutionary solution ever.

'So,' I said, 'what do you suggest?'

There was a very long pause.

And then a voice piped up at the back. It was Jonathan Fleming – the quiet lad who played Joseph in that rather eventful nativity play a while ago.

'Why don't we do another play?' he said. 'We could do it at Easter. We could tell the story and invite all our friends.'

And suddenly everyone started talking. Aruna started taking notes, Glenda began sketching out costumes and Giles was on his mobile organising a band. Jonathan – revealing hitherto untapped depths – was elected director and started calling everyone 'Darling'.

So that's it. We're putting on a play. Another play. Only this time without the Sunday school children and wholly devised and presented by the youth group.

What was it my mate said? 'When you start swapping stories, things happen.'

I somehow don't think this was what he had in mind.

Cheers

Chris

From: Chris Francis@Tabernacle.ch.uk
To: Patricia Ryan, P.Ryan@bigplace.com
Subject: The play

Hi Pat,

You'll recall that the group had come up with the idea of doing a play for Easter; a play about Jesus, to which they would invite their friends.

They wanted to handle the whole thing themselves. All I had to do was arrange the venue. The pastor was OK, and the church secretary was positively enthusiastic.

'I expect you'll be wanting an older woman to play Mary, the mother of Jesus,' she said.

'Er... I don't know.'

'Well, just in case, you might like to know that I spent 14 years in the Briglimpton Amateur Dramatic Society.'

'Did you?'

'Yes. I got some very good reviews, too. My Ophelia was much admired. And I have seen grown men reduced to tears by my Little Nell.'

There was a long pause.

'That's a character in *The Old Curiosity Shop*,' she said.

'I knew that,' I lied.

Dennis the treasurer was equally keen, providing, of course, that it didn't cost the church any money.

'Times are tight,' he said. 'But it's a good idea. You know, I've always seen Joseph of Arimathea as a more mature figure. I play Father Christmas for the playgroup every year and I used to do a lot of Shakespeare, you know. Grown men were reduced to tears by my Bottom.'

There was a very long pause.

'That's a character in *A Midsummer Night's Dream*,' he said.

'I knew that,' I replied.

Even Stanley the caretaker was supportive – and he hasn't agreed with anything the church has done since 1973.

'Used to do a bit of acting meself,' he said. 'Musicals and all that.'

'Don't tell me,' I replied. 'You played the Mother Superior in *The Sound of Music* and grown men were reduced to tears.'

There was a pause.

'Were you in the audience then?' he asked. 'Only I've still got the nun costume if you're interested.'

So, on to the rehearsals and I've never seen such a change as that which has come over Jonathan. Previously he wouldn't say anything to a goose, let alone 'boo', but the chance to direct has transformed him. He marched into the first casting session wearing a beret, carrying a megaphone and with one of those canvas director's chairs with his name stencilled on the back.

He has developed into what I think in film is called an 'auteur' i.e. he's written, produced and directed the whole show. Not only that but he also made the scenery and got his mum and dad to do all the refreshments.

The script was what you might call 'unconventional'. Purporting to show the last week of Jesus' earthly life, it included such settings as 'a club in Jerusalem' and 'the burger bar outside the temple'. The language was also contemporary, with one particularly ambitious scene being conducted entirely in text messages – flashed on to a screen above the stage.

'I've updated it a bit,' admitted Jonathan.

'Ah,' I replied. 'That explains why Jesus calls everyone "mate". And why Pontius Pilate declares that he's not going to do anything without a second UN resolution.'

'Sort of gives it a relevance, don't you think?'

The biggest difficulties came over the auditions for who would play Jesus. As the auditions went on it got more and more depressing. I wouldn't say the acting was wooden, but at one stage I suggested replacing everyone with railway sleepers on the grounds that we'd get a more animated cast.

After a while we began to discuss alternatives. Julian was of the opinion that any physical representation of Jesus was bordering on blasphemy, while Megan suggested representing Jesus by using a torch and shining it around the room.

Then a figure appeared in the room. It was Giles. He was wearing sunglasses, and a white T-shirt which he had sprayed with water in an attempt, apparently, to make it look sweaty. The whole effect was somewhat ruined by the fact that he was still wearing his usual corduroy trousers and a pair of sandals with socks.

He stood in front of us and adopted what he evidently believed was a suitably dramatic pose – although to my eyes it looked more like he'd been attacked by cramp. Suddenly, without any warning, he started to make a low, sort of grinding noise.

'Er... are you all right?' asked Jonathan.

'Mmbruughls mumbrggh hughhememm...' continued Giles.

'I think he's trying to act,' I whispered.

The audition continued, with his mumblings rising and falling, ending with Giles standing on top of the piano and yelling incoherently at the ceiling.

'Er... is there anyone with the gift of interpretation here?' I asked.

Later, it emerged that Giles had been watching the complete back catalogue of Marlon Brando films and had decided to play a kind of *Apocalypse Now* version of Jesus. Nevertheless, something in it seemed to inspire Jonathan.

'He's the one,' he said.

'He is?'

'Definitely!' exclaimed Jonathan. 'I tell you, I'm going to make that boy a star!'

I left the rehearsal and went home and poured myself a large drink.

Lucy came round.

'What's the matter with you?' she said.

'It's this play,' I said. 'I keep thinking of two words: "professional" and "suicide".'

'Don't worry,' she said. 'It will be fine. Just leave them to it. I'm sure everyone will find it very moving.'

'Grown men will be moved to tears,' I muttered. 'The only consolation is that hardly anyone will turn up.'

On the night of the performance I arrived at the last minute and was lucky to get a seat. The church was packed – and many of the people there were school and college friends, people I'd been trying to get to church for years. I didn't know whether to be excited that they were there, or appalled at what they were about to witness.

The lights dimmed. Then a group of Jerusalem residents appeared and started to discuss the arrival of this new teacher. Bizarrely, the inhabitants of Jerusalem included a man dressed as a nun, and Father Christmas. Suddenly Giles entered as Jesus, wearing an old sheet and a pair of sunglasses. Unfortunately, under the sheet he was still wearing his ordinary clothes. It was the first time I had ever seen Jesus wearing corduroys. Anyway, after asking if there was anywhere he could park his donkey, he announced that he was about to enter Jerusalem in triumph. Everyone started shouting 'Hosanna', Father Christmas started giving out presents and I started looking for the exit.

After that, however, things started to improve and I became aware that people were really getting into their parts. Vanessa played Mary Magdalene with her usual romantic gusto. I thought the scene when she poured the oil on Giles' Hush Puppies was very moving, although slightly marred by the fact that, when wiping it off with her hair, her wig fell off. And during the temple traders scene, Giles not only turned over the tables on the stage, but had to be restrained from rushing to the back of the church and knocking over the bookstall.

Something was happening. We should have been rolling in the aisles, but we were riveted to our seats. Something in this story was taking us – almost against our will – back 2,000 years to the terrible, wonderful events of that time. When the crowd shouted 'Crucify!' a chill went down my spine.

And then, they came to the crucifixion. I didn't know how they were going to do this. Nightmare visions of Giles on top of the piano came to mind, but it was wonderfully done. They simply lifted him up, one either side. No words. Backlit so that all was in shadow.

The pain was almost tangible. The sense of loss immense. A desolation. He was bringing us all back to what it was really all about. A God who chose to be helpless; a Christ in corduroys, lifted up for all of us.

And then, the joy of his return. The women and the empty tomb. The change from fear to wonder, from a terrified huddle, to a world-changing church.

This was a ramshackle, rambling, frequently ludicrous production. Hardly anyone knew their lines, the scenery had been put together overnight and the costumes were held together with string and sellotape. Everyone in the audience knew that, technically speaking, it could have been done a thousand times better.

But that didn't matter. It was real. It was a kind of incarnation, and you sensed that, perhaps for the first time, the cast and the audience were understanding something of the enormity of those events so long ago. Their weakness was strength; their sincerity and enthusiasm a channel through which God was speaking.

What was it my friend said? Things happen when people tell stories. Well, something happened in that church.

I looked about me, but my view was blurry. There was something in my eye.

Lucy smiled at me.

'Look at you,' she said. 'A grown man reduced to tears.'

Cheers
Chris

From: Chris Francis@Tabernacle.ch.uk
To: Patricia Ryan, P.Ryan@bigplace.com
Subject: New volunteer

Pat,

Sorry I haven't got much time to write this month. All a bit hectic with wedding plans and everything.

Great news, however: I've got a new volunteer. Jonny has just finished university and has come to work in the town. The first day he arrived in church you could see all the church leaders locking their radar in on him. The worship leader, the Sunday school leader, all the house group leaders – they all began to prepare their recruitment pitch. As soon as church was over the poor bloke was carpet-bombed with suggestions for ministry areas he could get involved in.

Of course I didn't join in. I believe in letting people settle in, giving them time to identify their calling within the body of Christ's people.

And anyway, I'd been round to his house the night before, helped him to move in and signed him up for the youthwork.

Cheers
Chris

From: Chris Francis@Tabernacle.ch.uk
To: Patricia Ryan, P.Ryan@bigplace.com
Subject: Re: New volunteer (2)

Sorry for the quick note. Still very busy.

Jonny has been a Godsend. He's great with the kids, has loads of creative ideas. I've been able to hand over a lot of this month's meetings to him which has given me time for everything else. I'm amazed by his energy – but then he is a bit younger than me. He's also got loads of ideas for the development of the youthwork. So we're going to have a chat next week.

Cheers
Chris

From: Chris Francis@Tabernacle.ch.uk
To: Patricia Ryan, P.Ryan@bigplace.com
Subject: Re: New volunteer (3)

Pat,

Still very hectic here, but things are a little easier. After a week off, I was back doing the Sunday night meeting again. Jonny has been a real success with the kids. If I didn't know better I'd say they looked a bit disappointed when they saw it was me running the session and not him.

Cheers
Chris

From: Chris Francis@Tabernacle.ch.uk
To: Patricia Ryan, P.Ryan@bigplace.com
Subject: Re: New volunteer (4)

Pat,

He's very young, of course. I must remember that. I probably didn't have much tact at his age. But I think I would have had slightly more tact than to sit down with the FULL-TIME OFFICIAL CHURCH YOUTHWORKER and point out to him where he was going wrong.

Not that Jonny put it like that. He couched it in terms of 'new ideas'. Some of which were very good. But all the same, I don't need criticism from the new boy. Not when I'm so busy with everything else.

Took the Tuesday night meeting tonight for the first time in a few weeks. Gave a little opening talk and then opened things up for questions. The first question? 'When will Jonny be back?'

Cheers
Chris

From: Chris Francis@Tabernacle.ch.uk
To: Patricia Ryan, P.Ryan@bigplace.com
Subject: Re: USURPER

DID I SAY 'NEW VOLUNTEER?' I MEANT TRAITOR, SNAKE IN THE GRASS!

I MEAN, HOW DARE HE CRITICISE WHAT I'M DOING? HOW MANY COURSES HAS HE BEEN ON? I'M A PROFESSIONAL. I'VE DONE MY TRAINING.

JUST WAIT UNTIL TOMORROW MORNING. HE'LL GET SOME SERIOUS SUPERVISION.

CHRIS

From: Chris Francis@Tabernacle.ch.uk
To: Patricia Ryan, P.Ryan@bigplace.com
Subject: Oops

Pat,

OK, OK, I know. It was late, I was tired. It gets to you, this job.

When I came here, I was the radical, I was the popular one. I was the one the kids wanted to hang out with. And, basically, that position hasn't been threatened, but it *felt* – and still feels – kind of threatening. I feel like the leader of the herd being challenged by the young buck.

When I asked Lucy what I should do about it, she replied, 'Have you thought about growing up?'

Still, I had a good chat with Jonny. He apologised for some of the criticisms he'd made. I apologised for feeling angry at him.

It'll be fine. I'm sure it will.

Cheers
Chris

From: Chris Francis@Tabernacle.ch.uk
To: Patricia Ryan, P.Ryan@bigplace.com
Subject: Et Tu, Jonny?

Hi Pat,

There's an old joke which runs: 'Just because you're paranoid, doesn't mean they're not out to get you.'

I have to admit I was a bit paranoid last month about Jonny, the new volunteer. Very confident, very popular, very, very, very, very annoying. But in the end, things settled down, and for a couple of weeks it's been fine.

And now it isn't.

Last night I was sitting with the youth group, trying desperately to make sense of Megan's latest mystical picture from the Lord, when Aruna suddenly said, 'He's right, you know. This group is boring.'

I didn't respond at once, mainly because, where Aruna is concerned, anything that isn't quantum mechanics or astrophysics is 'boring'. But the comment just lay there, itching away at the back of my mind, and after a while, I said: 'Who said this was boring?'

There was a pause.

'Oh, no one, really,' she said. 'Just someone I was talking to.'

So I let it go at that.

A few minutes later I was having another conversation, with a lad who had been playing up the week before – climbing on the roof. I was trying to explain what was, and was not acceptable.

'It was just a laugh,' he said.

'I look forward to witnessing your hysterics when you're lying in traction in the hospital,' I said.

'You're just a killjoy. Jonny was right!' he said, storming out. 'You don't understand us!'

I was shocked. What had Jonny been saying? I went back to Aruna.

'That "he" you were talking about,' I asked. 'Was it Jonny?'

Aruna looked like a cornered rabbit. She didn't reply. She didn't have to. It was a cheap trick to do, but I had to find out.

I went round to see Jonny immediately. I did this for two main reasons:

1) We're not supposed to let the sun go down on our anger.

2) I really, really, really wanted to shout at him.

But I didn't. Instead I tried to explain that, frankly, the job was hard enough without members of the team undermining what I was trying to do.

'I wasn't undermining you,' he said. 'I was just... well, you know, it can be a bit boring there and you do tend to over-react sometimes.'

'OVER-REACT!' I shouted. 'OVER-REACT!'

'You're doing it now.'

'No I'm not!' I said. 'Look, if you have criticisms of the way I do things, that's fine. But you talk to me about them. You don't discuss them with the youth group.'

'So you want me to pretend, is that it? Look, Chris, I'm sure you used to have loads of ideas, but the youth group as it is, well, it's hardly cutting-edge is it?'

There was a silence, during which the idea of 'cutting-edge' and 'Jonny' were combined in my mind in startling new images.

'We can discuss that, sure,' I said. 'But I want your promise that you are not going to discuss it with the youth group. If you're part of the team, we support one another. You can be part of the team, or part of the youth group. But you can't be part of both.'

'That's ridiculous!' he said. 'How are we supposed to get alongside these kids if we don't talk to them honestly?'

'I'd really like to continue working with you,' I said. 'You're creative, you're committed, the youth group like you, you get on well with them. But you have to understand there's a difference between being a leader and being one of the youth group.'

'And what if I don't want to do that?' he said. 'What if I don't want to take your orders?'

'I'm not trying to order you, Jonny,' I said, feeling suddenly both very old and very tired. 'I'm just trying to say that this is how a team has to work. I can't have you in the team if you're going to undermine me to the people I'm trying to work with.'

We left it at that. I don't know if he understood why I was upset. I don't know if he's going to change his ways at all.

Most importantly, if he doesn't change, then I don't know how I'm going to 'remove' him from the situation. I've always been desperate to get team members on board; I've never had to order one to walk the plank before.

So what do I do?

Cheers
Chris

From: Chris Francis@Tabernacle.ch.uk
To: Patricia Ryan, P.Ryan@bigplace.com
Subject: Goodbye Jonny

Hi Pat,

The Jonny saga seems to have come to a sad conclusion. After our run-in last month, things didn't really improve. There was more criticism about the direction of the youth group; even open opposition and disagreement in front of the kids. In the end I had to bite the bullet and ask him to leave the leadership team. I've had nicer experiences. Like root canal work.

In the end it came down to how we understood team responsibilities. I believed that he should not criticise team members to the youth group; he believed that he was only being honest. There didn't seem to be any common ground.

The whole experience has left me feeling a bit depressed, although I've since found out that it wasn't just me who'd experienced problems. Other members of the team had had similar experiences, and other church groups had also had problems. He'd upset Esmerelda Van Sant and the Sunday school workers by suggesting that the children needed more relevant role models. Mainly this seemed to concentrate on their age and/or fashion sense. I mean, the children love Esmerelda, even if she does dress like someone from the Laura Ashley catalogue and still has a fondness for the flannel-graph.

He annoyed Giles and the worship group by suggesting that their thrash metal version of 'Shine Jesus Shine' was not as cutting-edge as they liked to think. (Actually I'd have supported him on this. Giles' obsession with merging heavy metal guitar chords with worship songs is getting silly. Many of the congregation haven't recovered yet from his double-speed head-banging rendition of 'The Old Rugged Cross'.)

Anyway, I didn't know whether to be sad that he'd caused issues elsewhere, or relieved that it wasn't just me.

The most difficult thing was trying to explain it to the youth group, many of whom had grown genuinely fond of Jonny in the short time that he'd been with us. I didn't feel that, given all I'd said to Jonny, I could go around criticising him to the youth group as well. So I just said that we'd had differences about the way he'd been working with the team, so we felt it was better for him to take a break.

But the result of this is that somehow I've become the villain in their eyes. To them I am the ancient, gnarled head of the herd that has driven out the young challenger. It's not something that any of them have said, but you know how youth groups operate; the gossip flies around them faster than most government departments.

Nor has Jonny taken all this very well. When I told him that I didn't want him as part of the leadership team any more he didn't really say anything. He just grinned. I think the problem was that he has a veneer of maturity, beneath which lurks a bloke with all the maturity of a tadpole. I've been trying to talk to him; I've left messages on his answerphone, popped notes through his door, but all to no avail.

I keep wondering whether I should or could have handled this whole thing better. But all that stuff we did at college about conflict resolution seemed to peddle the idea that a bit of prayer and everything would be all right. Well, I have prayed about this, thank you. And it hasn't been all right. It's been painful and messy and I don't want to go through that again.

Last I heard he'd decided to leave the church and go to another one in the town. I did hear a rumour that he was going to St Hugh's. I expect we shall hear of the fallout in due course.

In the meantime it's the wedding in a few days' time. I wouldn't say I'm nervous; more petrified. Looking forward to seeing you there. I need a lift to take me away from all this, and I need some time off. This time next week I'll be sitting on a beach contemplating married life and sipping something that John Wesley would never have approved of.

Can't wait.

Cheers
Chris

From: Chris Francis@Tabernacle.ch.uk
To: Patricia Ryan, P.Ryan@bigplace.com
Subject: Back to life, back to reality...

Hi Pat,

Thanks for your note. I was really sorry you couldn't make it to the wedding. Hope you're feeling a lot better now.

Anyway, it was a great day. It all went by in such a whirl. I said to Lucy that we'd have to do it all again so I could remember it next time.

'Oh, don't!' she said. 'I don't think my family could stand another service like that.'

Her family – largely an unchurched lot – were completely bemused by the service. Come to think of it, I was completely bemused by the service. The pastor's sermon on 'Headship' was rather undermined when his wife told him to stop going on about it. Giles and the worship group's rendition of 'It is a Thing Most Wonderful' would have been better described as 'It is a Thing Most Incredibly Horrendously Loud'. And as for Megan's meditation based on Song of Songs...

But it was lovely to have so many of the youth group involved. Even Vanessa came, and I don't think she's ever forgiven me for becoming romantically linked with Lucy in the first place.

Anyway, it was a great day, made even more special by the presence of the young people – the people who have become my friends. Or so I thought.

We got home, after a fabulous three week honeymoon/holiday courtesy of Lucy's uncle who runs a travel company. First, I carried Lucy over the threshold of our new flat. Then I had a lie down while she rubbed some Deep Heat into the muscle strain that I had just sustained carrying her over the threshold.

And then the phone rang.

It was Sue, one of the youth group leadership team, who had been looking after it while I was away.

'How did it go while I was away?' I asked.

'Er... well, numbers were a bit down,' she replied.

'Oh,' I replied, feeling slightly smug at the thought that my absence made such a difference to attendance. 'Well, I'm sure that had nothing to do with me being away.'

'It had absolutely nothing to do with you being away,' replied Sue, swiftly puncturing my self-satisfaction. 'They've all started going to another youth group.'

There was a pause while my brain did a bit of processing.

'It's Jonny, isn't it?'

Jonny – the man for whom the term 'loose cannon' was invented (not to mention the terms 'arrogant loner', 'irresponsible gossip' and 'pompous fathead'. Of course, I might be slightly biased here.) Not only has he gone to St Hugh's, the Anglican church at the end of the road, but he's also started a new youth event there. And a lot of my crew have now started attending.

I phoned a few of them, under the guise of thanking them for coming to the wedding and all their gifts, etc. I broached the subject.

'Sue says we haven't seen you at youth group...'

'No,' came the reply. 'I've been busy', or 'I've been away', or 'I'm doing something else'.

Finally one of them came clean.

'No,' she said. 'Jonny phoned me and told me he was launching a new youth group at St Hugh's. So I thought I'd go and check it out.'

She then spent about 15 minutes regaling me with all the great features, benefits, innovations, joys, wonders, miracles and general marvels that formed the usual fare at the new youth group.

'Well, I can't tell you what to do,' I said. 'But this is your church. Don't you think you have a commitment to the people here?'

'I've been going to your youth group for years,' she replied plaintively. 'I just thought it would be nice to change.'

So there we go. This whole thing has ballooned out of all proportion. Not only is he a more popular youth leader than I am, but he is now deliberately headhunting my youth group.

Talk about coming down to earth with a bump. What should I do? Should I do anything? Should I try to talk to Jonny? Or should I just ignore him in the hope that he will simply go away?

Get well soon,
Chris

From: Chris Francis@Tabernacle.ch.uk
To: Patricia Ryan, P.Ryan@bigplace.com
Subject: Art for art's sake

Hi Pat,

Thanks for your advice over the situation with Jonny. Lots of discussions have been going on, but nothing has been resolved at the moment. (Well, I have resolved to kick him the next time I see him, but I may be talked out of that.)

However, one of the things that came out of the discussions was that maybe our teaching had got a bit stale. It was Sally – one of our Tuesday night team – who suggested that we should be a bit more 'art-oriented'. She is a sculptor in her spare time. (Her sculptures are strangely at odds with her character. She's a cheerful, quiet, gentle woman who produces sculptures that look like Dr Frankenstein's out-takes.)

Anyway, she suggested that we hold an 'Arts Service'. I put this to the pastor who looked doubtful.

'Some people want something a little different,' I explained. 'Not everyone learns in the same way, you know.'

He looked even more doubtful, but in the end he agreed that yes, we could have an Arts Service, as long as it was after the usual evening service on Sunday, and providing it wasn't actually called a service. But apart from that he was all for it.

So I left it to Sally. I arrived at the not-the-Arts-Service not knowing what to expect. Well, that's not quite true; I knew to expect some opposition, because Julian had been on the phone to me every night for a fortnight 'sharing his concerns'. So it wasn't exactly a surprise to see him outside the service handing out tracts by the Rev Murdo McBrightly entitled 'Art or Tart? Is Modern Art the Whore of Babylon?'

I knew also that, since Sally and Megan had been planning it, large parts of it were going to be largely incomprehensible, but even I didn't expect what I found on walking in. There were large sheets of black plastic hanging from the walls, on which a variety of paintings and images had been mounted. At the front was one of Sally's sculptures – a huge piece which looked like someone had attacked a garden shed with a tank.

I was equally unprepared for the assault on my senses that followed. First we all sang 'Abide with Me' to the accompaniment of Giles and his electric guitar. It sounded like he was playing a different key. Or even a different tune entirely. (Later I found this was, in fact, the case.)

Then we had some prayers, led by Megan, and a kind of interview in which Megan, at one end of the church, shouted her questions to Sally at the other end through a megaphone. Along the way, Sally tried to explain why her sculpture of rusty iron, tin cans, mousetraps and old dustbin lids was actually called 'Gentleness'. Then we had some more music, but this time were encouraged to simply go and look at the pictures on the walls and pray as we did so. Some spoke to me more than others, but I guess that was the point.

And what was amazing is that, amidst all this incomprehensible weirdness, people were really engaging. Kids whose general expression in church ranged from 'mild indifference' to 'complete boredom', were really working at their worship. And when we were invited to the front to do some painting, they really let rip. I saw kids splashing and painting and really expressing themselves and their faith; kids who normally hardly say a word. Admittedly I couldn't tell you what their pictures were about but they, and presumably God, knew.

I suppose the fact is that we use far too many words in our meetings. Art gets through the barriers, doesn't it? It gets people involved, on an emotional level. Whatever my reservations about the service you couldn't deny that God was there.

Cheers
Chris

From: Chris Francis@Tabernacle.ch.uk
To: Patricia Ryan, P.Ryan@bigplace.com
Subject: Which way now?

Hi Pat,

Have you ever had youthwork déjà vu? You know, that feeling that you're doing something exactly the same as you've been doing it before?

I'm not talking about saying the same things. I mean, that happens all the time. As one set of young people move on, to be replaced by another set with more or less exactly the same problems, of course you find yourself saying the same things.

I've lost count of the number of times I've had to say, 'Of course he doesn't hate you.' Or 'No, acne is not terminal.' Or 'Ignore what Julian wrote in that email: you are not predestined for eternal damnation.'

No, we all say those kinds of things. (Well, maybe we don't all say the Julian one, but he presents a set of very specific, recurring challenges). What I mean by youthwork déjà vu is that feeling that, not only have you used the same words, but you've just done exactly the same session as you have done before. You've covered the same theme, in the same way at some time previously. And this is not a deliberate copy. It's not that you are reusing tried and trusted material. It's that you couldn't think of anything new.

See, here's what happened. We'd revamped our schedule in light of the Great Jonny Betrayal Saga and put in some evenings looking at political and social activism. So I did one looking at the events in the Middle East. You know, some of the biblical background but also some of the modern situation.

The evening went well, although throughout the entire evening on the Middle East, I had this nagging feeling that I'd been that way before. (Not to the Middle East. But you know what I mean.) So, in the end I went home and dragged out my old files. And there it was: exactly the same discussion; exactly the same theme; exactly the same illustrations.

Now this is depressing for two reasons:

1) Because obviously the situation in the Middle East hasn't changed.

2) Because obviously I haven't got any new ideas left.

I don't blame myself for number (1) but number (2) left me feeling low. And the more I thought about it, the more depressed I got.

I talked to Lucy about it and she looked at me and said, 'Just think of something new, then.' Which is so very helpful. Roughly on a par with advising a man who has had his leg chopped off to 'stop bleeding'.

'I WOULD IF I COULD!' I shouted and walked out, slamming the door behind me for effect.

Anyway, she was more helpful later on, and advised me to have a look at all the resources I've stored up: you know, lesson plans, handouts, large books from impossibly cheerful Americans, that sort of thing. So I did that, but in a way they just made the problem worse.

I mean, the problem with resources written by experts in youthwork is just that: they're all written by experts in youthwork. These are people who are always putting together hugely creative, inspiring events, who enthral assemblies of 600 using only two cotton reels, a rubber band and an old sock.

So far from feeling empowered or inspired, I felt feeble and inadequate. Maybe the Jonny thing has knocked me more than I realised. The fact that so many of the young people from my group went over to his – although many are coming back now.

But maybe he was right. Maybe I am stale. Maybe I have reached the limits of my originality. We can recharge our bodies with rest and relaxation, but how do you recharge a brain? Where do I get creativity from when I've run dry? And will I ever have an original thought again?

All ideas, as they say, will be gratefully received.

Cheers
Chris

From: Chris Francis@Tabernacle.ch.uk
To: Patricia Ryan, P.Ryan@bigplace.com
Subject: New directions

Hi Pat,

Thanks for all the helpful advice about 'setting a new direction'. Yes, I think things have rather been pottering on here. Perhaps it's time to review the situation and chart a new course.

So, I've made a start. Or, more specifically, *we've* made a start.

I called a special meeting of the leadership team with the aim of drawing up a new direction for the group and adding in some new ideas. The leadership team has changed over the past few months – and, indeed, is still changing. But, although there are some new faces around, some things remain the same.

Here are the minutes from the meeting, as taken by Lucy, who, just this once, decided to help out.

BRIGLIMPTON TABERNACLE YOUTH GROUP STRATEGY MEETING

The meeting opened with prayer, worship and a 'prophetic gesture' from Megan. There was a short debate over what the gesture meant, with several people arguing that it was too obscure. Or even too obscene.

Following this debate the Chair (Chris) asked the committee what they wanted to see happen in the future.

Megan wanted to see us engage in 'greater intimacy with God'. Specifically through the use of chanting, incense, contemplative prayer and Ignatian meditation. Glenda wanted to see a greater use of biodegradable products and the provision of a crèche. It was pointed out that, as she is the only member of the youth group with a baby, this was more of a personal wish list. She responded that such a suggestion was 'babyist'.

Giles thought that we should expand the range of our worship – particularly with regard to something he was developing called 'Thrash

Worship'. This involves playing Graham Kendrick songs at twice the speed and with very loud guitars.

Aruna felt that we should engage in research so that we could produce evidence-based performance matrices and from there to launch a new market-driven portfolio of exciting youthwork products. She said that she had started to learn more about management following her being appointed to a new job. Giles pointed out that this job was selling shoes on Saturdays. Aruna said that she preferred to be called a 'Footwear Consultant'.

Julian told the group that in the next few weeks he was going to be spending some of his gap year working alongside the Reverend Murdo McBrightly at 'Save the World Through Calvin Ministries', so he would not be around so much. There was a brief smattering of applause followed by the Chair telling the rest of the leadership team to grow up. Julian then added that, judging from the spirit of persecution he had just discerned to be rampant in the group, he recommended we begin the year with a mass baptism in the local canal. He then went on to say that we should call people to (a) repent and (b) wear sandals.

Aruna said that if we wanted sandals, she could negotiate a high-margin discount on sandals for a bulk order. Glenda asked if they were vegan-friendly sandals and inquired if Aruna knew what the leather trade was doing to animals, not least to cows. Aruna called Glenda a naïve anti-capitalist. Glenda made a gesture at Aruna, which she then claimed was 'prophetic'.

The meeting was adjourned at 8:53 p.m. Date of next meeting 27th November. Venue 'The Meditation Room' (i.e. the large cupboard behind the vestry).

So there we go. In terms of charting a new course, I think it will be down to me again. Otherwise we'll all be wearing hemp sandals and listening to very loud guitar-playing.

Cheers
Chris

From: Chris Francis@Tabernacle.ch.uk
To: Patricia Ryan, P.Ryan@bigplace.com
Subject: Job or addiction?

Hi Pat,

Thanks for the phone call. Sorry I wasn't around, but I was out at a meeting. Again. I can't actually remember which meeting it was. It might have been the one with the pastor on the church strategy document (a long meeting, an even longer document, most of which can be summarised by the phrase 'Keep on doing what we did before.')

Or it might have been the one with the treasurer about whether the profits from the youth group tuck shop should be VAT registered. (I can't remember the outcome of this one either, although I think at one time he was suggesting that our pool table is subject to capital gains tax.)

It might even have been with the leaders of the youth group at St Hugh's who have now suffered the same fate that befell me with regard to Jonny. His arrival was met with great joy, then gradual disillusionment, and now he's moved on yet again, leaving a trail of hurt people in his wake. I suppose I should feel vindicated or something, but I just feel sad. He did try to move into Louise's youth group – you remember, the small bundle of energy who shadowed me. But she sussed him immediately and offered him the option of (a) going elsewhere or (b) having his legs broken. He opted for (a).

Anyway, you suggested I call you tonight, but I'm out at – you've guessed it – another meeting. This one has been called by the churches of the town and is entitled, 'Contextualising the Gospel Message for the People of Briglimpton.'

Tomorrow night I've got a youth group planning meeting, and then after that I've got to go on a pastoral visit to one of the young lads in the group. Then the next day I'm in school all day and then it's the regular meeting in the evening. Frankly, it's all getting too much. And Lucy is beginning to twitch whenever I mention the words 'appointment', 'work', 'meeting' or 'I'm just popping out for a moment'.

When I got in last night – about eleven – she was staring fixedly at the telly, with a stare that said, 'I am looking at this programme because I am far too angry to look at you.'

'Hi there,' I said, as casually as I could manage. The answerphone was beeping at me insistently, so I moved across to listen to the messages.

'Do you have to do that straight away?' she asked. 'You've only just got in!'

'But I ought to listen to the messages,' I said.

She turned and looked at me with the kind of eye-power that I usually associated with that bloke out of the *X-Men* who can send laser blasts from his glasses.

'The phone hasn't stopped ringing all evening,' she said. 'It's driving me mad.'

'Sorry,' I said. 'I'll just check them.'

I moved towards the answerphone again, but something in her expression stopped me.

'Don't. Touch. That. Button,' she said. I stopped.

'Er... no,' I agreed.

'You have been out every night this week, and you're out again for the next week as well,' she said. 'And when you're in you're checking the answerphone or emailing people or reading papers or planning projects. I am not your wife, Chris, I am your PA.'

'Look,' I said, 'you always knew I had a demanding job.'

'This isn't a job, Chris,' she said, 'it's an addiction.'

'Well, it's a busy time,' I said.

'It's always a busy time.'

'I know, but that's the job, isn't it? I'm not in that kind of job where I can just turn people away if they call after five o'clock. You know that and you've always known it.'

She said, 'Well, knowing it and living it are two different things.'

And she's got a point. It's never really been an issue before, but then I haven't been a married youthworker before. And I never really realised how intrusive it can be. So anyway, we've been through the diary and made a few changes – which is shorthand for scribbling through various appointments with a large felt pen. She's right. It is a job, but it can become addictive. And maybe the time has come to detox a little.

But also, it's made me realise how much I'm asking of my team. Maybe I've been critical of them when they've pulled out of things; maybe in the past I've been less than understanding when they've had other commitments.

Got to go now. I've been answering emails for an hour now and Lucy's coming towards the computer with a hammer...

Cheers
Chris

From: Chris Francis@Tabernacle.ch.uk
To: Patricia Ryan, P.Ryan@bigplace.com
Subject: Self-test results

Pat,

I'm developing a useful tool for all youthworkers. It's my patented 'Should You Still Be Allowed Anywhere Near Young People' self-assessment test. It's devised so that all youthworkers can check whether they should still be doing it. Here are just a few sample questions:

1. Do you still mind being out most evenings?

a) Yes

b) No

c) Not really, but I'd rather be at home watching the telly

(Score: a – 10 points; b – 0 points; c – 482 points)

2. Have you ever looked at *TOTP*/MTV/any Saturday morning chart show and said any of the following:

a) 'She'll get a cold wearing that.'

b) 'You can't hear the words.'

c) 'In my day they wrote tunes.'

(Score 10 points for any of these. Add a bonus 10 points if you've said all three during one programme. Add 50 points if you've said them all during the same song.)

3. Do you own any of the following:
a) a skateboard
b) a PlayStation
c) a Delirious! CD
d) a new carpet of which you're very proud and which no one can walk on without taking their shoes off?

(Score: a,b,c – 0 points; d – 20 points)

And so on. There are another 50 questions on my test list, but these will do for now. I reckon if you score more than about fifty you shouldn't be in youthwork any more. Anything over 300 and you probably shouldn't be allowed to do anything any more.

The interesting thing is that, although I score pretty low on my self-test, I'm coming to the realisation that my time is up.

If there's such a thing as an anti-calling, I've just had it.

This blinding realisation came to me yesterday, when I was sitting in a meeting with the pastor and Stanley the caretaker. Stanley was halfway through a talk on 'The Impact of Unchurched Young People on the Church Drainage System', when I felt God clearly telling me to 'get out'.

Of course, he could have been talking about the meeting, but I don't think so.

You know, I've never worried much about the idea of calling. It would have been nice, of course, to have received such a thing. It would have been good to hear a vast, spectral voice saying, 'Go ye and worketh among young people.'

But it never happened. And I went into youth ministry anyway, because that was what I really wanted to do and, as I think you told me at the time, 'Why wouldn't God want you to do what you want to do, if it's a good thing to do?'

But now I definitely have heard a calling. And God's telling me to go.

It's certainly not because things are going badly. On the contrary, the youthwork has never gone so well. We've got good numbers in all the groups, we're seeing young people come to the Lord and grow in their faith and really share their problems and issues.

It's just that, well, I don't think I should be here any more.

So I'm going to move on. Don't know how I'm going to do it, but I must. Because when God tells you to go, you go.

Am I right? How do you know when it's time to move on? And, more to the point, what am I going to do next?

Cheers
Chris

goodbye

From: Chris Francis@Tabernacle.ch.uk

To: Patricia Ryan, P.Ryan@bigplace.com

Subject: And now the end is near

Hi Pat,

I don't know why, but I was expecting more.

Maybe I would go outside and see that, although the dew was heavy on the street, my battered old Renault Clio was as dry as a bone. I was expecting... oh, I don't know what. It's just that, after all this time, I thought that the decision to leave was going to feel more dramatic. Instead, I had a series of pretty underwhelming encounters.

Episode 1: Lucy

When I told Lucy she looked at me and said, 'About time.'

'What do you mean?'

'You've been grumpy for ages,' she said. 'Everything about the job was annoying you.'

'Not everything, surely.'

'Pretty much everything,' she affirmed. 'I don't know much about these things, but I know that when you're not enjoying any of it, it's time to go.'

Episode 2: Stanley

I told the church in strict order of hierarchy. Which means, of course, starting with the caretaker.

'I'm leaving,' I said.

'Well, make sure you lock up properly,' he said. 'You always forget to lock the small lavatory.'

'I've always wondered,' I said, 'why do we have to lock the small lavatory? What's it got in it that people are going to want to steal? Is the toilet paper made out of gold leaf?'

'You can laugh,' he said, 'but I want it locked. I know about young people. They hide drugs in the cistern. I seen a documentary.'

'Yes, well, you'd have to be on drugs to want to use that toilet,' I said. 'Anyway, that's not what I'm trying to say. I'm leaving. I'm leaving the job.'

There was a pause. 'Ah,' he said. 'About time.'

'What's that supposed to mean?'

'Well, you stopped arguing with me ages ago,' he said. 'That was the first bit of fight I've seen in you for a long time. When you give up fighting for something, it's time to give up.'

Episode 3: The pastor

'I'm leaving.'

He gave a sigh of relief.

'About time.'

'What do you mean?'

'Well, you kept going blank in our meetings. I'd be saying something to you and you'd be staring off into the distance. Of course, that was nothing new when we were talking about general church matters, but about youthwork you always used to be really focused. And then you weren't. I always think that when you lose your ability to focus it's time to move on.'

Episode 4: Julian

To: Chris
From: 'Brother Julian'
Julian@savetheworldthroughcalvinministeries.org.uk

Dear Brother,

Just heard the news. About time. To my mind you have been predestined to move on from about a year ago. I had a vision involving you, a flaming sword, a mooring rope and a large watermelon. (If you wish to know the exact date of this message, I could look it up in my 'Visions Diary'.) I didn't realise what it meant until now. Now I see that it was time to cut the ropes that were tying you and float off into something new. (The Lord, as yet, has not vouchsafed to me the meaning of the watermelon. Perhaps it means you should become a missionary in southern climes?) I am well, thank you. I am currently attending a small, but I like to think elect, church called the Land's End Brethren. We're like the Plymouth Brethren only more extreme.

Yours through him, past them, with that and straight on till glory,

Julian

Episode 5: The youth group

I went in and called them all together. I was about to open my mouth when, almost as one, they said, 'You're leaving.'

'Er... yes.'

'Thought so,' said Aruna. 'You've spent ages making up your mind, haven't you?'

'Well, it wasn't an easy decision.'

'What will you do?' asked one. 'Where will you go?' asked another. And they followed it up with a host of other questions; involving things like who, what, why and when.

'I don't know,' I replied. 'I don't know the answer to any of your questions. I just felt that it was right to move on. It's not about you lot, it's not about the church, it's not about any of that.' I looked around them. 'It's just, well, you know. Sometimes it's the right time to go.'

There was a long pause. Then as if a switch had been turned off, they just went back to what they were doing. Chatting to each other. Playing on the PlayStation. Living their own lives.

I don't know why. I sort of expected more.

Cheers
Chris

From: Chris Francis@Tabernacle.ch.uk
To: Patricia Ryan, P.Ryan@bigplace.com
Subject: Know what I mean?

Pat,

I knew there was something I forgot...

Normally people have something lined up to replace the job they're leaving, but I've rather neglected that part of the process. The fact is, I haven't got a clue what my next career move is going to be.

Which wouldn't be a problem, except that people keep asking me, 'What are you going to do next?'

Of course, the true answer to this would include things like 'sleeping', 'not doing any youthwork on Saturday nights', 'not answering the phone', 'not doing any youthwork on Tuesday nights', 'having a holiday' and 'not doing any youthwork on Monday, Wednesday, Thursday, Friday or Sunday nights'.

But none of these are the kind of things you want to admit to people, so I've taken to telling them either that I will be 'exploring a few possibilities'.

It's not as though I haven't had a few offers. The first came from a friend of mine in a nearby town.

'So, what happens now?' he asked.

'Dunno really,' I replied.

'What do you think about the ministry?' he asked.

I laughed.

'Which ministry did you have in mind? I don't think much of the Ministry of Defence, for example…'

'You know what I mean – the proper ministry. Running a church. Grown-up stuff.' He snorted. 'I mean, all that youthwork is all very well, but now's the time to do some serious church work.'

There was a long pause.

'Well, that puts it all in perspective,' I said. 'I've been mucking about for the past few years, haven't I? I've been wasting my time with a load of frivolous church work. I should have been talking to adults, instead of trying to convert young people!'

'There's no need to take that tone,' he said. 'I mean you've done your apprenticeship. Maybe it's time you thought about working with adults.'

'I have been working with adults,' I replied. 'They're just not very old adults, that's all.'

'So I take it you're not interested, then?'

'No thanks,' I said. 'I'm not sure what youthwork is, but it's not an apprenticeship. It's much more than that.'

'Oh stop being so defensive,' he said. 'You know what I mean…'

'Yes,' I said. 'I know exactly what you mean.'

The second offer came from another youthworker in the town, who is setting up a youthworker training course based at his local trendy Anglican church.

'I wonder if you'd like to do some tutoring.'

'Well, what subjects are you talking about?'

'Old Testament Theology, New Testament Theology, Church History, Youth and Culture, Youth and Community, The Sociology of Youth Cultures, The Culture of Young Sociologists, Identity and Inclusion, The Impact of Modern Haircare on Youth Ministry, Schools Work and How to Avoid it…'

'Hold on,' I interrupted. 'What will you be doing?'

'Um… I'll be doing the paperwork.'

'What are you going to call this course, anyway?'

'We're going to call the scheme, 'St Nick's Offer Training To Youthworkers.'

There was a pause.

'Those initials spell SNOTTY,' I said.

'Oh,' he said. 'We'll probably have to change that. I'll get back to you.'

'I shouldn't worry,' I said. 'I don't want to do any teaching, thanks.'

'But why not? I mean, you've done your time. You've paid your dues. Now it's time to pass that learning on to others.'

'I wasn't paying my dues,' I said. 'You make it sound like some kind of punishment.'

'You know what I mean…'

'Yes. I know what you mean.'

The third offer came in a phone call from a friend who is working for a large Christian organisation.

'Hello, Chris,' she said.

'Hi there,' I replied. 'How are things?'

'Good,' she said. 'Just got back from a conference in the States. And I'm off to New Zealand in a few weeks time.'

'Give my love to the hobbits.'

'Yes, anyway, I was just ringing to find out if you might be interested in applying for a job with us. We're looking for a youth officer. Someone to head up our young peoples' ministries.'

For a moment I was interested.

'Tell me about it…'

'I thought of you, because, you know, what we do here has a global perspective. It would be a big move up for you, Chris. Talking to millions of kids. This is a new paradigm. We're not about just discussing what's on TV with a few kids in a small town. It's a worldwide, strategic opening. Really important.'

Suddenly I wasn't interested at all.

'Well,' I said, 'it's kind of you to think of me, but I think you've got the wrong bloke. You see, I like small towns. I like talking to kids about TV. You may be right, for all I know. Maybe it's not global. Maybe it's not talking to millions of people. But one thing I do know, it's been the most important thing I've ever done. So you can take your new paradigms and stuff them up your strategic openings.'

'There's no need to be like that,' she said. 'You know what I mean.'

'Yes,' I said. 'I know what you mean.'

What she meant, what they all meant, is that youthwork is fine, as far as it goes. I remembered my mum looking at me when I told her I was going to be a youthworker, and saying, 'But darling, where will it lead you?'

As I opened the doors for the last Tuesday night youth group, I could see exactly where it had led me. It led me here. It led me to this town, with these people. In some ways, it was nothing special. Aruna led a fascinating, if slightly confusing discussion on genetic engineering which concluded with everyone being against it, but if they *had* to have it, agreeing that people should either look like Justin Timberlake or Beyoncé. Someone hit someone else with a pool cue. Somebody else played a CD loudly. Stanley the caretaker came in and complained about the state of the toilets. We had the usual minor fallings-out, the usual rearranging of relationships, the usual opportunities to say something about God to people who really needed to hear.

But it mattered. It all mattered. (Except perhaps for the bit about the toilets.)

I'd said from the moment I announced I was leaving that I didn't want any special events. No parties, no farewell dinners, no speeches, none of that stuff. And that's what happened.

The kids went home; the helpers drifted off and I was left standing there, with nothing but memories. I remembered arriving here full of enthusiasm and naïve optimism. I remembered the fights I'd had with the treasurer to get the new pool table. I remembered the excitement of going to Romania. I remembered all those conversations with young people where we'd talk about their hopes, their dreams, faith, anxieties, beliefs, relationships… about anything and everything.

And suddenly I knew what youthwork was. I knew it wasn't a stepping stone, or an apprenticeship or some form of punishment. I knew it wasn't unimportant. What it was – what it is – is an adventure. I mean, what area of church life offers you so many extremes? It's either a white-knuckle ride, or a slog through a swamp. The highs are higher than anything else, and the lows are lower than you ever want to go, and in between there's joy and sadness, laughter and tears, hope and despair and more, well, more life than you know what to do with.

As I switched off the lights and stood in the darkness, all their faces seemed to rise before me; all the people I'd got to know. Glenda and her baby, Vanessa and her almost incandescent desire; Julian and his constant attempts to be martyred for the faith. There was Andy who had, against the odds, turned into my best helper, Jonathan and his plays, Aruna and her towering intellect, Megan and her mysticism, Giles and his excruciatingly loud guitar-playing.

I thought of the joy and the sadness, the successes and the failures. I thought of all the times I'd been puzzled by a question, stunned by a comment, overjoyed by a response. I remembered all the kids who said 'yes' to God; and all the others who had turned their face away. So many people. So much adventure.

I locked the door and turned to go. And there was Lucy, waiting for me.

'Hello,' she said. 'I thought I'd walk home with you. Thought you might need a bit of company, if you know what I mean.'

I nodded, tearfully. I knew exactly what she meant. The adventure was over. It was time for a new one to begin.

Youthwork the partnership

ALOVE (The Salvation Army for a new generation), Oasis Trust, Spring Harvest, Youth for Christ and *Youthwork magazine* are working together to equip and resource the church for effective youthwork and ministry. The partnership exists to offer support, encouragement and ideas for busy youth workers including:

Youthwork the conference

A weekend event designed for church-based volunteer youth workers, with specific streams for younger leaders and salaried youth workers. *Youthwork the conference* has been designed to give training and support by offering encouragement, ideas and resources to busy youth workers through main plenary sessions, practical and skills based seminars, opportunities to network, space to reflect and pray, and an extensive exhibition and resource area. *Youthwork the conference* takes place each November. Visit **www.youthwork.co.uk/conference** or call 0870 060 3327 for more information.

Youthwork magazine

Since 1992, *Youthwork magazine* has been the magazine of choice for youth workers across the UK. Every issue is packed with ready-to-use curriculum resources, book/CD/resource reviews; youth ministry and youth culture news and analysis, the lowdown on youth trends, challenging and inspiring articles, Jobsearch, must-see websites and more jammed into every issue, it's no surprise that so many youth workers consider *Youthwork magazine* essential reading. On sale in most Christian bookshops. Visit **www.youthwork.co.uk/magazine** or call 01892 652364 for more information or to subscribe.

Youthwork online

www.youthwork.co.uk features a dynamic home page updated weekly with the latest information, news analysis and views on youthwork and youth culture. Its also the place to find out about the partnership and how we can support you, including details on conference, magazine, training courses, and resources. At www.youthwork.co.uk/community you'll also find a range of online discussion forums where you can discuss youth ministry issues and share ideas and resources with other youthworkers from across the country. Visit **www.youthwork.co.uk** for more information.

Youthwork the radio show

Youthwork the radio show is broadcast on Saturdays, 3.30pm-4.00pm, on Premier Christian Radio, in London on 1305 1332 1413 MW, and nationally on Sky digital Channel 873, ntl Channel 886 and Freeview Channel 96. Hosted by Martin Saunders, the show features interviews with leading youth ministry figures, creative ideas for youth ministry, up-to-date news about youth work and trends in youth culture, and music to help you resource your youthwork.You can also listen in on the web any time at **www.premier.org.uk/youthwork** or **www.youthwork.co.uk** where you'll find the latest programme, plus an archive of previous programmes.

Youthwork the resources

A series of books edited by Danny Brierley and John Buckeridge. The series includes three types of books: *Developing Practice* titles are designed for all those engaged in youthwork and ministry. They are inspirational and practical without being overtly theoretical. *Going Deeper* titles are designed for those who are serious about youthwork and ministry. They are sometimes controversial, always challenging, but never dogmatic. *Resourcing Ministry* titles provide busy youth workers with tried and tested ideas and curriculum to use with their young people. Visit **www.youthwork.co.uk/resources** or call 01825 769111 for more information.

Youthwork the training

WHAT EVERY VOLUNTEER YOUTH WORKER SHOULD KNOW

A training course for busy 'extra timers' who need to know the basics – and fast! This innovative course provides a foundation of knowledge, tips and resources in an accessible and practical format. The course is made up of 9 two-hour sessions which may be delivered in a variety of ways to fit your needs and lifestyle. Participation includes a free resource book and 100 ready-to-use ideas. The course is endorsed by a broad spectrum of Christian denominations and networks. Visit **www.youthwork.co.uk/training/volunteerscourse** or call 020 7450 9044 for more information.

THE ART OF CONNECTING

A resource to equip you and your youth group to see lives changed... forever!

The vision behind 'The Art of Connecting' is the realisation that people communicate most naturally when they are exploring their own stories together. The course aims to empower people to share their faith through story – making connections between their story, their friends' stories and God's story. 'The Art of Connecting' book and Leaders Pack are available, as are regional training days for youth leaders and young people. Visit **www.youthwork.co.uk/training/aoc** or call 0121 550 8055 for more information.

Oasis Trust

Drawing on 20 years experience of pioneering mission, education and youth work initiatives; Oasis provides opportunities for young people to participate in life changing UK and Global mission (*Frontline Teams; Global Action Teams & Passion*) and equips youth workers with pioneering resources and training (*What Every Volunteer Youth Worker Should Know* course & JNC-qualifying *Youth Work and Ministry Degree*). Oasis also enables youth workers and church volunteers to support young people's personal, social and health education in their local schools through our Oasis Esteem program, while tackling social exclusion among young people head on through Oasis Youth Inclusion.

To find out more about Oasis:
Visit: **www.oasistrust.org**
Email: **enquiries@oasistrust.org**
Phone: 0207 450 9000
Write to: Oasis, The Oasis Centre,
115 Southwark Bridge Road,
London, SE1 0AX, England.

ALOVE – The Salvation Army for a new generation

ALOVE is The Salvation Army for a new generation. ALOVE is calling a generation to dynamic faith, radical lifestyle, adventurous mission and a fight for justice. ALOVE provides young people and young adults with ongoing opportunities to engage in culturally engaging worship, cell and small group discipleship, innovative mission and world changing social action. ALOVE runs training programmes to develop leaders and missionaries for the 21st century. ALOVE is also pioneering new expressions of church, youth work and social inclusion in communities around the United Kingdom and Ireland.

To find out more about ALOVE:
Visit: **www.salvationarmy.org.uk/ALOVE**
Email: **ALOVE@salvationarmy.org.uk**
Phone: 0208 288 1202
Write to: ALOVE UK, The Salvation Army, 21 Crown Lane,
Morden, Surrey, SM4 5BY, England.

Spring Harvest

Spring Harvest's vision is to 'equip the Church for action'. Through a range of events, conferences, courses and resources we enable Christians to impact their local communities and the wider world. Spring Harvest is probably best known for the Main Event, held every Easter, which attracts over 55,000 people of all ages, including over 10,000 young people and over 2,000 students. Alongside the teaching programme, Spring Harvest provide a range of resources for young people and those involved in youth ministry.

To find out more about Spring Harvest:
Visit: **www.springharvest.org**
Email: **info@ springharvest.org**
Phone: 01825 769000
Write to: Spring Harvest,
14 Horsted Square, Uckfield,
East Sussex, TN22 1QG, England.

Youth for Christ

Youth for Christ (YFC) are taking good news relevantly to every young person in Britain. They help tackle the big issues facing young people today by going out on the streets, into schools and communities, and have changed the lives of countless people throughout the UK. Their staff, trainees and volunteers currently reach over 50,000 young people each week and have over 50 centres in locations throughout the UK. They also provide creative arts and sports mission teams, a network of registered groups and a strong emphasis on 'three-story' evangelism. YFC International works in 120 nations.

To find out more about YFC:
Visit: **www.yfc.co.uk**
Email: **churchresource@yfc.co.uk**
Phone: 0121 550 8055
Write to: YFC, PO Box 5254, Halesowen,
West Midlands B63 3DG, England.

Youthwork magazine

Youthwork magazine is Britain's most widely read magazine resource for Christian youth workers. Through articles, ready-to-use resources, reviews, youthwork and cultural news and analysis, and much more, *Youthwork magazine* provides ideas, resources and guidance to help you in your work with young people. *Youthwork magazine* is published monthly by CCP Limited, which is part of the Premier Media Group, who also publish *Christianity* and *Christian Marketplace*.

To find out more about *Youthwork magazine*:
Visit: **www.youthwork.co.uk**
Email: **youthwork@premier.org.uk**
Phone: 01892 652364
Write to: Youthwork Magazine,
CCP Limited, Broadway House,
The Broadway, Crowborough, TN6 1HQ, England.

YOUTHWORK
M A G A Z I N E